PRO

Bruce Hamilton

'Pro' tells the story of Edward Lamb, professional cricketer and son of a professional cricketer. It will be enjoyed not only by lovers of the game but also by all those who appreciate a human drama encompassing hope, triumph, setback, recovery and eclipse.

When Edward's father dies penniless, the boy goes to live with unsympathetic relatives. The 1914 war, in which his closest friend is killed, robs Lamb of the period during which he should have developed as a cricketer and leaves him with neither glory nor money. His success as the first bowler to exploit leg theory brings him an invitation to join the MCC touring the West Indies, but in the first match he is seriously injured. On his return he finds that his wife, a frivolous and extravagant woman, has squandered his money and been unfaithful.

Edward's protracted fight against recurring misfortunes has an almost epic quality. When it was first published, John Betjeman, writing in the *Daily Herald*, said of this novel: 'This book is not only knowledgeable and interesting about cricket, it is also a subtle character study of the relations between "amateur" and "professional"'.

Other
Outstanding
Titles
in this
new series

---

by G. C. Foster

FULL FATHOM FIVE
RAHAB AND RACHEL

by L. A. G. Strong

THE ENGLISH CAPTAIN
THE JEALOUS GHOST
THE GARDEN

7 5 11

Bruce Hamilton

PRO

A HOWARD BAKER BOOK
Published by
Howard Baker Publishers Limited
in association with
REMPLOY LIMITED
NEWCASTLE-UNDER-LYME, STAFFORDSHIRE

Bruce Hamilton

PRO

This Howard Baker Edition, 1970

SBN 09 308390 4

First published in Great Britain by
The Cresset Press, 1946

Howard Baker Books are published by
Howard Baker Publishers Limited,
47, Museum Street, London W.C.1
in association with
Remploy Limited,
Newcastle-under-Lyme, Staffordshire

Printed in Great Britain by Photolithography
Unwin Brothers Limited
Woking and London
And bound by Remploy Limited in Wales
at Ystradgynlais, Glamorgan

I

TO EDWIN WILSON LAMB, from as far back as he could remember, cricket had not been so much the most important thing in life as one of the chief governing conditions of life.

Thus there was in the first years of continuous thought-association nothing very magnificent about the conception of a professional cricketer. One's father might go to cricket of a morning, in the same way as one's friend's father went to the office, or to the shop, or in rarer cases to "business". The world's work was carried on by cricketers, in the same way as it was carried on by engine-drivers, or doctors, or butchers. It was possible that one inherited an aptitude, and on the chance of this part of one's earliest domestic education was given a particular bias. But ideas of play, of pleasure, of glamour, or of excitement entered into the matter just as much as, no more than, such ideas inhabited the first discussions and tentative preparations for the career of any boy.

That any difference in kind was recognisable in such a career was made manifest for the first time on Teddy's first morning at Somerset House, during the eleven o'clock break.

The headmaster had taken him into the study to give him a school cap. A difficulty had arisen in finding him one of the right size, resulting in a late appearance in the boot room and the holding up of "the walk round the back" while he tugged nervously at the tag of his right boot, which he had unlaced insufficiently, and which would just not go on. Mr. Roberts was a new master just as Teddy Wilson was a new boy, but neither was aware of the other's novelty. Therefore Mr. Roberts, who understood that it was necessary to get the upper hand of the boys at once, relaxation of severity being only permissible when the ideal of discipline had been attained, spoke sharply to the boy. Teddy did not resent this. He was unused to the idea of injustice. But he was depressed; his morning had been a mystifying one, with the point of the first examples of Henry's Latin Grammar entirely eluding him; and he saw no familiar faces. Unaccountably the Archer boys, whose parents' recommendation was responsible for his presence at the school, were both absent. He scurried along by himself, a yard or two before Mr. Roberts, accelerating every few moments as the master called out, "Get on! I won't have any lagging behind!" Unreasonable as this was, for Mr. Roberts moved at a smartish pace for his five feet ten, Teddy again experienced no resentment. Plainly it was quite in order that the boys should trot their walks.

A little out of breath, after about ten minutes of this, he was suddenly called on to consider the advances of a squat boy, no taller than himself, but obviously four or five years his senior. A friendly approach was indicated by the offer of an acid drop, which Teddy somehow managed to detach from its neighbour with the addition of a quantity of paper.

The boy asked with commendable directness:

"What's your name?"

"Lamb."

"How old are you?"

"Nine." Homage to truthfulness impelled Teddy to add, "Next week."

The older boy found these answers fair enough.

"I'm Baker," he volunteered. "You seem to

be the only new bug this term. Have you been to school before?"

"No."

"I'll look after you for a bit then."

"Thenks awfully," Teddy replied.

"Why do you say 'thenks'?"

"I didn't, I said 'thenks'."

"There you go again, 'thenks'. You should say 'thanks'. Go on, say it properly."

"Thanks."

"That's better, but you haven't got it quite right. Are you common?"

"No, I'm not common."

"You sound rather common."

"I'm not."

"What's your father, then?"

Teddy deliberated before answering. But Baker seemed well enough disposed—judicial and objective, rather than censorious.

"He's a cricketer," he answered.

"Fool," retorted Baker. "I'm a cricketer. I mean what does he do for his living?"

"He's a cricketer."

"Do you mean a pro?"

"Yes."

"You're not trying to be funny, are you?"

"No, honest injun. He's a cricketer."

"By Jove!" Baker exclaimed suddenly. "You don't mean to say your father is Baa-Lamb?"

"He is called that. But it's not his name."

"Good Lord!"

The walk was almost over, and Baker was overcome and silent for the rest of it. But in the quarter of an hour before lunch—and indeed for the rest of the day—Teddy was astonished to discover that he was the centre of interest.

Almost the whole school seemed awed—it is hardly too strong a word—to learn that this slender, shy child, with fair hair, a longish face tapering to the chin, and rather girlish eyes and mouth, was the son of the famous all-rounder "Baa-Lamb", the pillar of the Midhamptonshire County Eleven. Teddy was asked for the most intimate details about his father's private life; what he ate for breakfast, whether he used wax on his moustache, was he decent or was he ratty, did he ever lam Teddy, how much money did he make. All these questions the boy answered patiently and to the best of his ability. And because, both now and later on, he made his responses with becoming modesty, showing no disposition to exploit his glamorous if somewhat equivocal parentage, he quickly became popular at school, although never a leader. This modest lack of pushfulness was a quality he retained throughout his school career, for although not clever he was able to apprehend intuitively the reasons why he was so well liked. He never allowed his school-fellows to realise what a revolutionary change in his own outlook had been inaugurated on his first day at school; how his love and admiration for his father had, by swift degrees, been transformed into sheer idolisation; the extent to which eminence at cricket had become the pinnacle of all worldly ambition.

Somerset House was, of course, not without detractors of this sort of greatness. The prospectus of the school announced it as preparing the sons of gentlemen for the Public Schools and the Navy. With rare exception this boiled down to the Midhampton Grammar School or a job in an office; nor was the gentry unimpeachable, being of a shabby and threadbare kind even in the most favourable cases. In truth Somerset House was a cheap and dingy school, making pretensions it could never quite live up to. But just as the greater world contains no persons more inflexible in exacting due tribute of respect from inferiors than those in a state of suppressed doubt about their own superiority, so a third-rate provincial prep school is seldom without its exponents, mostly parent-stimulated, of a like vigilant snobbery.

To such it was clear that the companionship on equal terms of the son of a professional cricket player—by definition no gentleman—was something of a slur on themselves. The instinctive democracy of children, helped by Teddy's own quiet and unobtrusive amiability, prevented this section from ever becoming really strong.

Nevertheless, meaning references to talent money or playing for one's average, or pros swilling beer between innings at the County Ground Tavern, were heard on occasion. Teddy never rose to the bait. But anyone supposing he was too dense or insensitive to take in the implication of such sneers would have been greatly in error.

II

TEDDY's father was certainly, by no valid standard of social criticism, in any way "common".

His origin was indeed modest enough. He was head gamekeeper at Burrington Park, about twelve miles out of Midhampton. The interest of the Malverns of Burrington was traditionally paramount in the country, and none born within the orbit of the virtually feudal economy of the family and content to remain there ever had occasion to consider the future. No doubt young Albert Edwin Lamb would have stepped comfortably into his father's shoes, but for the chance that the fourteenth Earl of Malvern was, although a more than indifferent player, a passionate lover of cricket. The Burrington Week in September, just before the shooting began, was a booked date for half the Gentlemen's eleven of the period, and a prize for the best Public School players of the season, hardly second in consideration to an invitation to play for a county.

When young Lamb was first picked for Eighteen of Burrington against Lord Malvern's Eleven, at the age of fifteen, he was looked upon as a promising bowler, but not believed to harbour ambitions about the game beyond the ultimate attainment of a small local celebrity, and in the meantime of earning a few more half-crowns at the nets than the other young men about the place. Nevertheless, the ambitions were there; it was not for nothing that he had watched some of the greatest players in the country, year after year, from the time he was considered not big enough to play with a hard ball. He rose to his opportunity, taking 7 of the distinguished guests' wickets for 39 runs on a perfect Burrington wicket. Events in the following year showed that there had been no fluke about the performance, and his reward came, before he was eighteen, in the form of an engagement on the ground staff at Lords. After a four-years' apprenticeship in London, playing constantly in company of class, he returned to his native county. The Earl and some other gentlemen had, after a few false starts, succeeded in getting under way a regular county club, and young Lamb was one of half a dozen professionals engaged to play for it.

The venture was a success, and from the beginning Albert Lamb was never in any doubt as to his ability to make good in the career of his adoption.

In those days, the early eighties, the county championship was still something of a close corporation. Midhampton played a few matches every year with the more powerful teams, but ranked as a minor county. The feasibility of these combinations has always been a near thing in the best of circumstances. The club did not pay its way, being kept alive by the generosity of wealthy patrons, but it returned a dividend in the form of interesting cricket, sometimes reaching a very high standard. In 1895, when the scope of the championship was widened, Midhampton obtained recognition as a first-class county. For a year or two the team did very well, holding a comfortable position in the first half of the table. Afterwards it fell away. The batting strength which had made it so formidable declined as the older players grew too old, or were unable to give their full time to the game, and adequate successors were not forthcoming. From the last year of the nineteenth century down to 1905, when Teddy left Somerset House, the side was a very ordinary one, capable of brilliant performances, but without solidity.

It was in these years that Albert Lamb—or "Baa-Lamb," as he was affectionately called by his fellow players and the Midhampton public—rose to his position as the dominating figure in the side. Of the other professionals who had assisted at the birth of the club, some had been older men who had retired in the natural course of things, others promising youngsters whose promises had not been kept. Albert alone remained, growing ever riper in skill and experience, becoming, in fact, one of the major figures of the game. Except for one year when he was out of form after a strenuous tour in Australia, and another when a leg injury kept him out of the game for most of the season, he turned out regularly for the Players. He never made his mark in international cricket—his one overseas tour had shown that the Australian atmosphere was not heavy enough to permit the peculiar late swing that made him so deadly when there was any moisture in the air—and in his two appearances in the Tests in England, while not altogether failing, he did nothing of note. But as a county cricketer he was in the very first rank, seldom getting less than a hundred and fifty wickets a year, and later, as the need for run-getters became painfully apparent, developing his batting enough to place him regularly second or third in the county averages. It was no exaggeration to say that for the last ten years of his life he carried the team on his shoulders.

They were broad enough for the burden, in these later days. The slender boy who had bowled down the guests at Burrington by sheer heart and speed was now neither slender nor boy-like, and he had given up fast bowling within a year of his going to Lords. The contemporaries of Teddy at Somerset House were worshippers of a hero of about forty, of majestic, almost corpulent build, but very light on his feet. His habitual bearing had a sedateness which to a later generation would have seemed more proper to a man of fifty. He wore a heavy black moustache, slightly upturned at the ends—an innocent and pleasing vanity. His dark hair, seldom seen on a cricket field, where he was inseparable from his cap, was still very thick but grizzled. His flannels were always spotless and beautifully turned out, if impalpably old-fashioned in cut, but he wore the modish sash, or rather large dark blue handkerchief doubled to a point, making a triangle below his waist behind. He was always ready with his autograph, and generally had an amiable word or two for the petitioner, spoken in a voice that was curiously deep, gentle, and cultivated. His upturned moustache blended with the lines of his face to give the effect of a perpetual smile, and indeed geniality was radiated from the man—not a boisterous geniality—rather a serene Olympian kindliness.

On the field his individuality was strongly marked. The Somerset House pupils were familiar with, and prone to imitate Baa-Lamb's bowling—run and action—nine short springy paces on tiptoe, the arm coming over high, close to the ear, and very quickly. They well knew that rubbing together of his hands before the final crouch in the slips. Even more characteristic was the rotating of his upturned bat as he looked round the field, almost naively, before taking his first stance; and his stance itself, a deep crouch, moving smoothly just before the bowler delivered to a secondary position, upright, the bottom of his bat raised to the level of the bails. He always looked a fidgety opener, given to little mannerisms, such as feigning an attempt at an impossible run, or, when a ball had beaten him, leaning on his bat and contemplating his blockhole in apparent abstraction for five or six seconds. He liked a joke on the field and he was not ashamed to repeat his effects. One of his favourites, particularly in home matches, was to run almost half-way to the pavilion when his wicket had been thrown down, pretending to be out; and he would raise his bat in acknowledgment of the relieved laughter as he trotted back.

Such was the man seen by Somerset House; and, indeed, though a degree or two nearer life size, by the whole of the Midhampton cricket public. The style was in truth the man, expressing perfectly his zest, his warm-heartedness, his innocence, his modesty, combined with a clear awareness of himself as a public figure. Naturally Teddy, viewing the matter from a closer range, felt the impact somewhat differently. His first idea of his father was not of a giant in a green field, but of a quiet pipe-smoker in shirt-sleeves, pottering round a back garden; a lovable figure indeed, who never raised hand or voice to him; but sometimes rather depressed, and frequently, in the summer, desperately tired.

Albert Lamb was a widower. His wife had been, rather oddly, English governess to the children of a French consular servant. She had travelled with the family to places as far apart as Bucharest and Mexico City, and her marriage might be considered as an abdication of superior social standing. It was nothing of the kind, for Martha Wilson belonged to that class of governess whose style and accent debar them from engagement with English families, but who are easily able to find employment on the continent or in the United States. She was, however, a good teacher, and brought up her charges to speak the English of Balham with some fluency. Albert had met her at a whist drive in South London in his M.C.C. days. She had fallen in love with him at sight and had gradually accustomed him to the idea of an engagement. She was considerably older than Albert, who had not at first been at all willing. The marriage was delayed some half-dozen years, but once the step was taken he quickly fell into a state of utter and willing dependence on her. Of this she was entirely worthy. As a wife and during her brief period as a mother, she proved herself devoted and selfless.

Edwin was born in 1890. Two years later his mother died, after being delivered of a still-born girl. Edwin did not recollect her at all. As far as he was concerned, her place at home was taken by Aunt Stella, Albert's elder sister; a good-hearted but managing and quarrelsome woman who provided him with the discipline which his father had neither the ability nor the inclination to exercise.

Albert, indeed, made a shy father. Sometimes, particularly in the winter, when he had nothing much to do except keep himself fit, he would have moods in which he was a delightful companion. He played a good game of bears, and his personality came out strongly at hide-and-seek, while the hanging of Christmas decorations, and indeed the whole festival, always found him in splendid form. But then at Christmas time he would have a few friends around, with a few drinks inside, and he was always at his best in company. Alone he was apt to brood, sometimes hardly opening his mouth for days. He should perhaps have re-married, but he never felt strongly enough towards any of the young women who would have been glad to have him to break down a rather perverse idea of loyalty to Martha's memory.

One fine April, when Edwin was five, Albert bought a small bat, stuck a Tate's sugar box against the garden wall, and began tossing up lobs to Teddy with a rubber ball. He avoided too much instruction, insisting only on a straight bat and a left leg carried to the pitch of the ball. The lessons were continued intermittently, and became more advanced. Albert would occasionally bowl a leg-break, which Teddy never failed to miss.

"Why did you miss that one, Teddy?" he asked once.

"It went crooked."

"All right, now I'm going to bowl some more crooked ones. Try and stop 'em."

Teddy tried, and, so long as he knew they were going crooked, met with some success. Then Albert started to bowl straight again, and when, a dozen balls later, a crooked one came along, it thudded against the sugar box.

"Here, I thought you could play those now," exclaimed Albert.

Teddy protested, "I didn't know it was coming."

"Ah! that's the question," said Albert. "Next thing you've got to do is, learn when they're coming. See if you can find out."

Sure enough, Teddy found out. Evidently the crooked ball was sent down in a different way. He watched his father's hand, and presently spotted the trick. He waited for the next leg-break, and pushed it clearly to the off.

Albert beamed. "Now you're a cricketer."

He did not let him bowl much at this stage, holding that a young child was unfitted for the artificial action of getting the arm over straight. But he taught him to catch, and run, and pick up, and throw accurately.

When he told Edwin he was going to school—Albert was a careful man with a benefit to look forward to, and felt able to give his son an education that cost money—he said:

"You'll probably play a better game than most of your age. But don't get uppish. It's nothing much, playing cricket well. You stick to your Latin and Arithmetic."

He had ideas of a scholarship—perhaps eventually Oxford or Cambridge, and a blue. He wanted Edwin to be a gentleman.

III

EDWIN was, however, not clever. "Just fair", or "I think he is trying " were about the most favourable observations ever to figure in his termly report sheets, but it was more often "Rather weak", or "More concentration needed". He had little mental staying power, being unable to fix his attention on any problem for long, but he was not without intelligence, and would have responded to careful teaching methods. Unfortunately, teaching at Somerset House had no method at all. In the hands of the three assistant masters (£50 to £60 a year resident) Mathematics became the illustration of, and the exhortation to reproduce, processes that were never explained, Latin a dull puzzle, French the deadest of dead languages, Geography a matter of Capes and Bays, History of dates and names, with a shrewd question-spotting boy, who could hardly have scored in a proper test, able to get full marks lesson after lesson.

Teddy, therefore, in common with all the other boys except the handful who had the trick of lessons, came to look on schoolwork as a tiresome routine. It was clear in less than two years that a scholarship was out of the question. Albert's dreams had to be abandoned. By this time he had taken his benefit, which had been a great deal less successful than he had hoped, and with retirement from the game inevitable within a few years, he had to think of the future. He knew that employment as a coach or an umpire would be open to him as long as his health and strength lasted, but such posts provided hardly enough to permit saving. And the accumulation of money had now become a major preoccupation with him, not in any miserly spirit, but because he was determined that his boy should not be forced into uncongenial labour by lack of resources.

The true reason for his anxiety was that he knew Teddy was resolved to follow in his footsteps, but had no confidence in the boy's ability to make good. He saw that the game was going to become even more commercialised, bringing a spirit of competition and ruthlessness which would allow no mercy to those unable to stand the pace. Teddy, at the age of eleven or twelve, seemed by no means robust. He was always catching colds, he got tired too easily, and, in spite of all the joints, steaks, chops, and potatoes with which he was assiduously plied, the child remained painfully thin. The headmaster of Somerset House was breezily re-assuring. "Nothing to worry about; he's just outgrown his strength for the moment," he said. But Albert believed he knew better. The boy was lacking in stamina; it had been just the same with his mother.

It was not that he lacked promise as a cricketer. In fact it was Teddy's very aptitude, coupled with a marked absence of signs of talent in any other direction, that reconciled his father to giving the boy his head.

Teddy first played for Somerset House before he was ten—an honour without precedent, though perhaps due more to his father's name than his own playing effectiveness. For two years he did nothing much, never getting more than twelve or fifteen, but always looking a player. In his third year he took a big leap forward, and in this and his last year at school he scored and took wickets almost as he liked.

The cricket he played was in fact too easy for him. But it happened that there was at school a boy named Cecil French, a year Teddy's senior, who was quite an exceptional all-round games player. He was a big fellow, unhandy with his schoolwork, and inclined to be a bit of a bully. As with Teddy, his social standing was precarious; and it was perhaps this circumstance, added to sheer admiration for his strength and physique, that had drawn the younger boy towards him from the earliest days.

French, however, was at first by no means disposed to reciprocate this feeling. He was, in fact, desperately jealous of Teddy. A boy whose bluster was really only the mask for an extreme sensitiveness, he cherished his athletic supremacy as the one gift which made him stand out from his fellows and think well of himself. It compensated for his ugliness, for his stupidity, for his poverty, for the dirty shirts and socks his poverty and his own lack of management compelled him to wear, for the insults and laughter he received at the hands of his masters and schoolfellows when he made howlers in class. Never mind—he could run faster, jump higher than all the rest of them, knock the stuffing out of them at all games. And now he saw his nose put out of joint by a boy little more than half his size, whose cricket had a style and fluency he could never aspire to, and whose father was not an underpaid clerk in the office of the Midhampton Borough Council, but the one man whom he reverenced above all others. It was not fair.

It was touch and go whether he would love or hate Teddy. He decided to hate him.

The result was that he made Teddy's life as uncomfortable as possible. He had no real cruelty in him, and physical abuse was not usually his method. But he became adept at inflicting small pin-pricks, hiding his books, breaking his pencil-points and crossing his pen-nibs, jerking ink on his clothes. Teddy bore it all with fortitude. There was nothing heroic about him and he knew very well that any attempt to fight French could only have one end, and might set a precedent for further corporal humiliations.

One November afternoon, as the boys were changing for football, French began throwing Teddy's clothes about. Mr. Roberts, who was on duty and supposed to supervise the changing, was for some reason absent. There were always two or three ready to play up to French, and the joke ran for about five minutes. By this time all the other boys were changed, and soon clattered off to the field. Teddy was left behind, and was presently discovered, struggling into his shorts, by the headmaster.

"Late again, Lamb," said the headmaster. "Well, you can't say you haven't had a fair warning. Come upstairs."

"He gave me four," confided Teddy to the half-back who was marking him, on the field ten minutes later. He could not quite bring himself to tell French what happened, but he wanted him to know. Sure enough, French looked particularly sheepish for the rest of the afternoon. After prep, when the day boys were going home, he sidled up to Teddy as the latter was climbing the steps from the boot-room up to the street.

"I say, man," he muttered, "is it true the old swine gave you four?"

Teddy answered, "Yes, man. Didn't hurt though."

French ruminated.

"Not bad of you not to sneak," he tried.

"Rot, man," Teddy replied. He began to feel a warm glow.

They were walking along together, although it was not French's way. After a few moments' silence, French brought out:

"Sorry I was such a swine, man."

"No, you weren't."

"Oh, well. Sorry anyway."

Teddy thought it was his turn.

"That was a jolly hot goal you shot this afternoon, man. From that corner."

"Oh, rot, man," French answered. "Only a fluke."

"I thought it was jolly hot."

"No, it wasn't. That was a jolly fine run you made down the wing though, man. You know, when Thompson fouled you."

"Oh, that was just luck."

It was becoming a love scene. A few minutes later French took a further step forward—almost equivalent to a proposal.

"I say, man. What about coming to tea at my place Sunday?"

"Wouldn't mind, man. Thanks awfully. Is it all right?"

"I'll ask the mater and tell you to-morrow. It'll be all right."

"That'll be fine, man."

"Mother's soda-cakes aren't bad."

"You must come to tea at my place some time."

"Wouldn't mind, man. Would your dad be there?"

"Yes, he'd be there all right, man. He's always there, in the winter."

"I *say*, man. I wouldn't mind meeting him."

"He's not bad," admitted Teddy.

IV

THEREAFTER the two formed a community apart. There were certain reserves between them. It was many years before they could bring themselves to call each other "Cecil" and "Teddy", even in each other's homes. French had inherited a taste for evangelical religion; Teddy liked reading, particularly the historical novels of Harrison Ainsworth and the scientific fantasies of Jules Verne. But attempts to express their feelings on these matters broke down, and they had at last to tolerate in each other idiosyncrasies privately thought unaccountable.

Their friendship, however, could have withstood the strain of far less trivial differences. It was founded on the rock of a love of cricket that transcended the normal, a passion that was intellectual and romantic even more than it was physical. Their reaction to a table of averages resembled that of a chemist to a newly evolved formula; the staccato account of a day's play in the *Evening Courier* was like a beautiful lyric discovered by a lover of poetry; action pictures of Ranji or George Hirst had the excitement of a Sargent exhibition to a contemporary connoisseur. They were inmates of *arcana* beyond the reach of their simple schoolfellows; when the rest of Somerset House held itself quite sufficiently technical in referring to sneaks, and blocking, and slogging, and plugging, French and Teddy were thinking and talking in terms of off-theory and body-break, flight and footwork. Separately, they might have been mocked and put down as swankpots, together they were invulnerable.

They were not above relaxation of this high austerity. On wet half-holidays, they would play "cricket on paper", shutting their eyes and jabbing pencils on behalf of the players of Midhampton or Gloucestershire (it was strange how seldom Gloucestershire or its equivalent managed to win). One Christmas holiday they discovered at Henchard's toyshop a game called "Cricket at Home", which was really a kind of roulette, with singles, fours, twos, rarer sixes or threes, and the different methods of getting out, distributed with a nice realism. It was possible to play swift matches over by over, and get very plausible total scores and results; but it was also possible to cheat; and the game finally lost favour owing to a defect in actuality irreconcilable with the exacting standards of the manipulators. For alas! there were no legitimate means by which tail-end batsmen could be prevented from scoring as heavily as the openers, and too many centuries from Numbers Ten and Eleven destroyed the look of the score-book.

Of course, the authentic game was something more than a scholar's preoccupation or a parlour amusement; it was only that there was so much more time available for thinking about it than playing it. But play it they did, with spectacular effect. They brought Somerset House undefeated through their last two seasons, bowling practically unchanged and getting between them eighty per cent. of their side's runs. Between them there was now no suspicion of jealousy, nor could there be any occasion for it. It was impossible to say which was the better. Teddy was the more accurate and thoughtful bowler, and always looked the more genuine cricketer. French played like what he was, a superb athlete who excelled at all games rather than a specialist; but his batting was more effective, and his greater strength and hostility made him, in general, a stronger match-winning force.

More dear to them than school matches—which were, after all, little better than playing with rather unchivalrous remorselessness against girls—were the long golden afternoons of those last two summer holidays. Somerset House played their games on a corner of the county ground, and this gave the pupils not only the right of free admission to all matches, but the privilege, modified by the frequently surly temper of Goddard, the head groundsman, of playing privately in the holidays, provided one got in no one's way.

In retrospect, there always seemed to Teddy to have been something indescribably moving about that holiday—he was to go to the Grammar School next term. It was a glorious August, day after day of deep burnished indigo skies without a cloud. The county had three or four home matches, watched by the boys from the side of the screen, or sometimes from near the professional's pavilion, where the demeanour of the heroes, emerging to bat, hopefully, or indifferently, or nervously, and returning with elation, nonchalance, or dejection, could be studied at close range. The two boys spoke very little, and resented the ignorant chatter of children and fools around them. At lunch-time they brought out their sandwiches, munching in a deep trance-like satisfaction, and presently their silence would break down into monosyllabic comment. Then the first bell; the clearing away of ropes, vacuous inspectors of the pitch, and flying boys with tennis balls; the slow umpires' procession; and, at last, the cricketers again, bringing another deep hush.

Tea was the climax of the day. They needed drinks, and had nothing left from lunch. They would thrust in competition with the men at the bar, opposing to the stentorian calls for bitter, weak appeals for ginger-beer and a pennyworth of Garibaldi biscuits, fussing in their fear that they would not get back to the game in time. Afterwards, the shadows of the pavilion, and of the elms behind it, advanced stealthily to the wicket, the white gold of the atmosphere became a yellow gold, and presently it was half-past six. Outside the ground there was a civil exchange of good-byes—"Same time to-morrow." Each had spent a perfect day, perfectly companioned.

But more often there was no match at the ground, or no match worth watching. Then French would be round at half-past ten with his private knock on Teddy's front door. Teddy was generally waiting, with bat and ball ready, and they were soon up at the ground. At the north end, behind the screen and in front of the tennis courts, they would improvise a wicket, with a blazer and a broken chair. Till one o'clock they batted and bowled, at intervals resting flat on their backs, their faces upturned to the sky. Then it was time to go home again to dinner, but before half-past two they were at it again. The bar was closed when there was no county match, but it was hardly worthwhile going home for tea. Towards five they would climb, bat and all, over the spikes of the closed gate at the north-east, and go to Carter's little shop a few yards away for doughnuts and Penny Monsters. Teddy, the affluent one of the pair, nearly always stood treat. The seriousness of the last hour of their day, after they had scrambled back, was somewhat relaxed. They might play French cricket, or even not play at all, but watch, in convulsions of ill-stifled merriment, the ridiculous antics of the lady archers, who were hated because they had certain rights on the north end of the ground, and sometimes made themselves a nuisance.

V

ON THE LAST DAY of the last home county match of the season, a weight, too deep for expression, lay on the spirits of both boys. The shadow of the world's harshness hung over their idyll. On Monday, French was to go to work as an office boy at Mercer's, the wholesale grocers. Teddy indeed had three weeks more holiday in prospect, but nothing to do with it, and a dark tunnel awaited him too, at the end. He was used to Somerset House. He did not look forward to starting all over again, without French, at the Grammar School. Also, he was not happy about his father. Albert was worried and out of form, and talked gloomily of retirement. Once or twice he became irritable over trifles, a thing hitherto absolutely unheard of. One evening he lost his temper with Teddy, and brought him to tears. The occasion had been so trivial that he quickly realised he had been unjust. "Don't mind, little fellow," he said, awkwardly consoling. "It's things on my brain. I don't seem as if I can get them off."

Presently he added:

"I've made a bit of a mess of things, Teddy. It'll be all right though, if we go slow." This meant nothing to Teddy.

Midhampton were on the field, this last day of the season, and they had to prevent Essex from getting 313.

The sun was very hot. By lunch, three wickets were down for 97. Except for twenty minutes rest Albert had been bowling the whole morning. He had taken no wickets, but he had kept the batsmen very quiet. He had bowled like a tired man, using all his experience and mechanical skill to compensate for his lack of physical energy.

He continued after the interval. Perrin and Macgahey were batting, looking very determined, very settled, very unlikely to get out. The heat had become terrific. Maiden followed maiden from Albert's end. But the score crept up. At 160 he went off. Runs came more quickly at once. At tea-time Essex had made 219, with Perrin and Macgahey still there.

"We're going to lose," prophesied French. "Unless your dad gets going pretty quick."

"He's tired," protested Teddy. "They have to bowl him too much."

French nodded, "He's not a chicken, either."

The comment was no more than the obvious truth. Teddy had heard the same sort of remark before, from odd people in the crowd. But coming from French it hurt. Albert was only forty-five, and he had always said that a man who looked after himself should be able to last till fifty. W. G. had scored 70 odd for the Gentlemen at fifty-seven. Teddy suddenly experienced a passionate desire for his father to do something out of the way to refute the silly calumny.

After tea Albert was given the new ball, which had been kept back for him to use when he was fresher. He bowled a maiden, Macgahey took three from the other end—and then things began to happen.

Macgahey played forward just inside the second ball of the new over, and Tanner made a very good catch low down at second slip. The next batsman was clean-bowled first ball. The situation was entirely changed, and the change was reflected in the demeanour of the crowd. It became alert, the intense heat seemed less oppressive, as apathetic resignation to defeat gave way to almost painful hope.

"Doesn't look as if he's finished yet," said Teddy.

Albert was bowling with a devil he had not shown the whole day. It may have been the very strong tea he habitually drank, perhaps he owed something to the moral stimulus of a quick wicket. The ball was going where he wanted, moving in the air and fizzing off the pitch with ferocity. He got a wicket in each of his next two overs. Then Perrin came down to his end, and set himself to knock Albert off his length. He left the wide outswingers, but got right over the straighter ones and drove them to the off.

Albert changed his field. He put three men close in on the leg side, leaving only one slip, and began to swing the other way. The move at first seemed negative, for the inswinger combined with the offbreak, pitching on the off or the middle stump, went away to clear the leg stump easily. It was quite safe to leave them alone.

Then he bowled one a little faster with top-spin that neither swung nor broke. It hit Perrin on the pad, and he was given out.

It looked as if the game was won. Essex still wanted 74 with only two wickets to go. Everyone hoped Baa-Lamb was going to crown his triumph by finishing off the match himself.

But after the incoming batsman had taken his guard it was evident all over the ground that something queer was happening.

Albert had been sitting down in a normal attitude of relaxation after the fall of a wicket. He did not get up. Arthur Meadows, the captain, went up and spoke to him. Albert made a gesture, as if waving him away; and then he seemed to change his mind. He got to his feet. One ball of the over remained to be bowled. Albert moved up to the wicket and with great labour brought his arm over. Then he sat down again.

They carried him off the field.

Teddy had never been allowed in the professionals' pavilion before. Even now he felt shy about entering it. At the top of the stairs he met Shelly, the twelfth man, a tall, freckled boy of nineteen.

"You'd better not go in, Ted," he said. "The old man's a bit shaky—you can't do any good."

"Please let me go," said Teddy. Shelly let him pass.

Albert was lying on the floor. His head was supported on a pile of blazers, and his arms and legs were twitching. His face was the colour of dirty paper, and something seemed to have happened to the left side of it. He was conscious, and was quite obviously making painful, terrible efforts to get up. His fellow players were trying to soothe him and someone held a glass of water to his lips. No one paid any attention to Teddy.

Presently Dr. Littlehampton came, and soon after the ambulance waggon from the hospital. The game went on; Shelly went out to field with the rest. They let Teddy ride in the ambulance. They got out of the ground only just before the crowd, the last Essex wicket falling as they passed through the gates.

Albert died about fifty hours later, without speaking another word. He was unconscious most of the time, and it was doubtful if he recognised anyone around him.

VI

AT BREAKFAST one morning, a day or two after the funeral, Aunt Stella said with false cheerfulness:

"You know, my lad, I'm afraid you won't be able to go to the Grammar School."

"I don't know that I mind that," Teddy answered.

At the moment, beyond the cardinal fact of loss, there was nothing much that he minded. His life had been unhitched from its anchorage, and ever since the funeral he had been moving about in a daze. He had nothing to do with his time, until about six o'clock, when he would wander round to Mercer's and wait for French to come out. Presently French would appear, sometimes quite late, with a basket of letters. He would nod to Teddy, "Won't be a sec, man," and disappear towards the post-office. He had to go back to his office, to hand in registration slips, but quite soon he was out again.

"Come on, Ted."

They had at last reached the stage of Christian names. French had made the advance. It was the nearest he could get to condolence.

They walked off, arm in arm, towards French's home. Their way lay by the county ground, but by tacit consent they made a little detour to avoid it. The golden weather had broken, and a boisterous south-westerly wind, bringing occasional scuds of rain, smashed in their faces. They had not much to say, but came to life a little in each other's company.

"How's the old office?" Teddy might ask.

"Not bad."

Teddy understood that "not bad" could signify a multitude of things, according to context and intonation. Here he rightly interpreted it as meaning "very bad indeed".

"Going to get any footer?" he tried.

"May play for the Church Boys on Saturdays. When they let me off."

Teddy sighed. "I wish we were grown up, Cecil."

"You're all right," French pointed out, "you're going to the Gram."

"Don't know that I want to," Teddy replied.

"Don't be an ass, man. You'll be all right—after a week or two. Don't suppose I'll see much of you."

"Oh, rot."

Teddy indeed could hardly be convinced that the Gram was not just another trap waiting for him. So when his aunt told him the project was off he took it with apathy, even relief. But Aunt Stella had not finished. Presently she added:

"You'll have to think about going to work."

By degrees the mischief came out. Teddy learned in what respect Albert had made "a bit of a mess of things". He had been induced to invest the proceeds of his disappointing benefit, added to his life's savings, in a speculation that had gone the wrong way. His total property, at the time of his death, was discovered to be some worthless certificates of the Inca Mining Corporation, the furniture in the house, and forty-five pounds in the bank. Teddy's position was as bad as Cecil French's; in fact, it was worse, for Cecil at least had a home to go to. Albert's home had been rented, and there would be no rent forthcoming after the current quarter.

At his age, Teddy was incapable of appreciating the seriousness of financial disaster. His expectations had never been other than of earning his living as soon as he left school; the idea of unearned increment did not enter his horizon. The fact that he was leaving school much earlier than intended seemed to make no difference in principle, if anything it was an occasion for relief.

When it came to the question of what he was going to do, the situation looked less simple. Cecil French had put him off offices. He didn't want to think too much about cricket at present, but he had not, of course, lost his ambition to play for Midhampton. At his age, however, it seemed unlikely that he would be any use to the club in any capacity. After some self-examination he went to see the Secretary, Mr. Gilbert, who had spoken pleasantly to him on the ground once or twice.

Mr. Gilbert was sympathetic, but not very helpful.

"How old are you?" he queried.

"Thirteen, sir."

"Well, you can see for yourself you're too young for the ground staff."

"I wondered if I could sell cards. Or help with the telegraph."

Mr. Gilbert shook his head.

"There wouldn't be a living for you, Teddy. Even if we could make a job—and it's the wrong time of the year at that. You see, we are running on a small adverse balance year after year, and we simply have to watch every penny."

He filled his pipe.

"I'll keep my eyes open, Teddy. Maybe I'll hear of something to suit you round town. We owe a great deal to your dad. Hasn't your aunt any ideas?"

"She wants me to go on a farm. Cousin Phil's, at Burrington."

Mr. Gilbert jumped at it.

"Seriously, that would be just the ticket. Give you a

chest measurement and put a little flesh and muscle on those bones of yours."

He pinched Teddy's arm. "You take my advice and go on your farm. And come back to see me again in three or four years, when you're a big fellow. No promises, mind. But we'll give you a good try-out, and if you're your father's son, you'll make good all right."

He gave Teddy half a sovereign.

VII

IN THE END, the farm had it. Teddy did not like the idea. He was a town boy, and envisaged work on a farm as heavy and dull. Also, he did not care much about Cousin Phil. But Aunt Stella was persistent, and he had no alternative to offer.

Just before Michaelmas the furniture was sold, an unseemly and riotous climax before Teddy said good-bye to the only home he had known. His luggage and Aunt Stella's had already gone on by the carrier. At half past four, as the street lamps were being lighted, they climbed on the horse bus to the station. The inside was full, and they had to go on top. Teddy led the way to the front of the knifeboard. Old Mays, the driver, raised his whip.

"Well, Master Ted," he observed, "so we're off."

"Yes, Mr. Mays. Off at last."

"Ah!" Old Mays shook his head. "Well, we all have to be off sometime."

Unexpectedly, Cecil French was waiting in the booking-hall when they reached the station.

"Hello," he said. "I thought I'd come round."

A lump came to Teddy's throat.

"Hello, Cecil. Coming on the platform?"

"Might as well."

Aunt Stella got into a third non-smoker when the train came. They had five minutes to wait, and the boys walked up and down the platform. There was nothing much to talk about.

"Won't there be a row when you get back?" Teddy asked.

"S'pose so. Don't care, though."

"At any rate they can't whack you."

"No. Only sack you." The boys laughed hollowly.

Too soon the guard came, with his green flag. Teddy was coaxed into his compartment.

"Well." Cecil swallowed. "You might send a chap a letter."

"I'll send you a letter. You might too."

"I'll send you one all right."

The whistle blew, and the train moved off.

"'Bye, Miss Lamb. 'Bye, Ted."

"'Bye, Cecil."

Teddy leaned out of the window, and waved his handkerchief. Cecil waved his hand. He had left his handkerchief at home.

VIII

Cousin Phil was a man whose presence was so formidable, whose behaviour in general was so coldly beastly that, at the rare moments when he relaxed into geniality, a boy was almost hypnotised into loving him. There have been fathers and schoolmasters of that sort.

A week after his arrival at Burrington, Teddy was at a job of digging in the Long Bottom field, when he became aware that his cousin was behind him. He already knew enough not to stop work, but his fingers were mauve with cold and the surface of the earth half frozen; he was making very little impression on it. Presently he ventured to look behind him, to find the farmer's great purple face convulsed with mirthless, silent laughter.

"Scratching like an old hen!" he gasped, "like an old hen!"

"Scratching like an old hen." Teddy heard plenty of the phrase during the following weeks. Cousin Phil hardly let a meal-time pass without contriving an excuse to mock Teddy with the silly image, always brought out with the same dull vindictive laughter. Once Aunt Stella said rather tartly, "Haven't we heard enough about that, Phil?"—but no impression was made. "Like an old hen—huh—uh—uh—uh."

Cousin Phil had been on his horse at the original encounter, a bay cob, very strong, as indeed it had to be to carry its rider's sixteen stone. Out of doors, Cousin Phil was never seen off his horse. His legs were bad, and he could not walk more than a few yards. His mounting of the beast had a certain grandeur. A block with three steps raised him to the level of the horse's back; there was a man to support his elbow, and another to hold the cob's head. The process was reversed when he got down.

When he was put out, he never raised his voice, but fell into a cold, silent, kingly rage that might last a month. From this state he would emerge one day, without warning, into a sunlight of warm good humour which was such an overwhelming relief that it seemed to compensate for weeks of thunder. His customary close-fistedness would relax as though touched by a quick thaw; libations of beer and cider would be poured upon the field labourers, Teddy would get half a crown or a day's holiday in Midhampton, Aunt Stella a brooch, and Mrs. Phil a new dress or a new pair of shoes.

For the first year Teddy and Aunt Stella lived at the farmhouse. From a domestic point of view the place was shockingly run. Mrs. Phil exhausted her energies in finding for her husband the immense meals he required; everything else went hang. She was "artistic", and the whole house was covered with bilious relics, in water colours, of her creative period. Phil had fallen in love with her and proposed when she had come to Burrington on a sketching holiday, but he had given her no hint of the sort of life she would have to lead as his wife. The approach of disillusionment had been rapid. After a few years she took to consoling herself with gin, soon perfecting a talent for secretly absorbing enormous quantities without giving overt signs of her condition. Unless, that is, anything occurred to upset her. Once that happened, there were ructions, and the cat was out of the bag. It was an incident of this kind that led to Aunt Stella and Teddy leaving the farmhouse. Aunt Stella had, by tactful degrees, been taking a more and more active part in managing the household, and one evening she gave a servant an order in ignorance that a contrary order had been given by the mistress. Mrs. Phil heard, and, giving no credit to the ignorance, revealed herself as what, at the moment, the poor woman was—a drunken harridan.

The row was patched up; but it was agreed that it would be better for the Lambs to leave. Cousin Phil found them a cottage in the village; they collected a little furniture, and made out. Teddy was making 12*s*. 6*d*. a week, and Aunt Stella had forty pounds a year of her own. She also did sewing for Burrington House, and was generally kept fairly busy. She was, however, becoming less easy to live with. Her temper was sharper than ever, and she suffered a great deal from stomach pains.

Meanwhile, Teddy continued to regard his work about the place with a dull dislike that sometimes reached the point of disgust. He hated farm smells, farm dirt, farm clothes. Though he was always in bed by nine he loathed dragging himself up at half-past four or five, and never seemed to catch up with the sleep he wanted. His days were mostly passed in a stupor, and he felt himself growing daily more earthy and beastlike. He was shy of the labourers, whose speech and manners were alien to him, and he had no other companionship. Sometimes he would hardly open his mouth to speak all day; and when he got back to Aunt Stella of an evening he was too exhausted for much speech, too exhausted to do anything but bolt his food, look over the sports page of the newspaper, and clump upstairs to bed. His life meandered on like a long, uneasy dream.

Certainly, after the first year, he found the sheer bodily endeavour less heart-breaking and back-breaking. His muscles became adjusted to their tasks, and he acquired enough technical skill to save unnecessary effort. His health, too, improved. After a first winter of constant snuffling, he seemed to shake off his propensity to colds.

He gained in weight (though very little in height) and his colour became clearer. At fifteen he had lost most of the rather feminine comeliness that had been his two years before, but he looked twice as robust and physically effective.

He always saw Cecil French in his rare days in Midhampton, and one Sunday Cecil came on a borrowed bicycle to see him. They were a little shy of each other, and therefore talked more than had been their habit. Cecil had grown enormous. He was still at Mercer's, now ranking as a junior clerk, but was making very little more money. He had, however, more time for games, and was doing well in junior cricket and football. He had been promised a trial for Midhampton Wanderers, the town's leading amateur football club. When Teddy told him he got no cricket, all he could say was, "Good Lord".

It was true that, for the first two summers, Teddy did not play at all. The old Earl was dead, and the game at Burrington had died with him. A village eleven still hurled and smote on the Green most Saturday afternoons, but Teddy had no time to play for it. Sometimes he got worried, and was haunted by a neurotic fear that he would never get back any form, that when he presented himself to Mr. Gilbert he would play like a clodhopper.

One Sunday in April, about thirty months after his arrival in Burrington, he tackled Cousin Phil as he was getting on his horse after church, and asked without preamble:

"Can I have Saturday afternoons off?"

Cousin Phil was in a comparatively good humour. He looked down doubtfully.

"What for?"

"I want to play cricket."

"Cricket won't get you anywhere."

"I want to play. I want to try for the County next year."

"So you want to be a cricketer."

Uncle Phil considered.

"Suppose I give you Saturdays. What will you give me?"

"You could take off some of my wages. Or I could work on Sundays."

"You could, could you! Well, you'll never make a farmer. We'll see, we'll see."

In the end Teddy got his Saturdays, for nothing.

At first, it seemed as if his worst apprehensions were going to be realised. On the rough and ready wickets of the Green, good defence was at a discount. He might make five or six in twenty minutes, before succumbing to some aberration in the pitch. Finally he decided to chance his arm and trust his eye, and then did better, but the biggest score he ever made was 37. Towards the end of the season, however, his bowling began to come back. He found that to get wickets regularly all he needed was a controlled length, a little variety in pace or flight, and equanimity in respect of dropped catches. He achieved some startling analyses; and one August afternoon an astonishing portent was seen, nothing less than Cousin Phil, cob and all, planted on the edge of the Green in front of the "Queen of Spades". The old man had heard stories of the lad's prowess. Teddy rose to the occasion by getting 7 for 12, in 7 overs.

Next Monday they started on the hay. As Teddy was helping to pile a stack, Cousin Phil rode up to him.

"You're mortal slow," he grumbled.

Presently he went one, "Maybe you're right, wanting to be a cricketer. You remember your dad, though. Hold on to what you get."

Teddy worked through the winter with a lighter heart. Next April he packed up and went to Midhampton. He had less than six pounds saved, but Cecil's parents had agreed to board him for a while, at fifteen shillings a week. For three weeks, every fine evening, he had practised bowling in the garden of the "Queen of Spades". If he failed to take his chance, it would not be due to any early-season stiffness.

IX

HE WAS in such a ferment that he could not wait until next morning to get things started. Also, there was a faint cloud of anxiety on his horizon. A fortnight before he had written to Mr. Gilbert reminding him of their former talk, stating that he was coming back to Midhampton, and expressing the hope that he would be given a trial. No answer had been received. His letter did not actually call for an answer, but it had been chilling not to receive one.

After supper, when grace had been said, and the boys were left on their own, Teddy said:

"I say, Cecil, I thought I'd go and see Mr. Gilbert. Come along with me."

Cecil demurred.

"You go alone, man. I'd only be in the way."

"Come along, man. Come and back me up."

"Well. I'll come to the house with you. But I won't go in."

Teddy well remembered the house, a couple of doors from St. Patrick's Church in Holland Square. With a little cajolery he prevailed on Cecil to remain at his side as he rang the bell.

"Can I see Mr. Gilbert, please?" he said to the maid who opened the door.

"Mr. Gilbert?"

"Yes, please."

"There ain't no Mr. Gilbert here. This is Mr. Cummingses."

"Doesn't Mr. Gilbert live here any more?"

"No." The maid had a Cockney intonation, and pronounced the word "Now". "This is Mr. Cummingses."

"But, please, can you tell me where Mr. Gilbert does live? He used to live here."

"Now. Don't know at all."

A clergyman with a moustache came to the door. He was dressed for the street.

"You boys want me?"

"Please, sir, we are looking for Mr. Gilbert."

"Mr. Gilbert? He's not here now. Walk along with me, will you? I'm in a hurry."

The clergyman strode off at a violent pace.

"Didn't you know?" he asked. "He left Midhampton—went to South Africa last November for his health. We're living at his house while the Rectory is being rebuilt."

Teddy rallied to ask who was the secretary of the County Cricket Club.

"That chap—what's his name? Don't tell me." Mr. Cummings snapped his fingers. "Jordan—yes, that's his name, Jordan. I believe he lives somewhere in Denver Crescent. I'm afraid I don't know the number."

Denver Crescent was at the other end of the town. They got there in half-an-hour. At the third house they attempted they were given Mr. Jordan's number—in Wilson Avenue, a few streets away.

In the end they drew a blank. Mr. Jordan was out, and not expected back till half-past eleven. The boys went home to bed.

The next twelve hours were a nightmare. After an almost sleepless night, Teddy presented himself at Mr.

Jordan's home at ten o'clock. Mr. Jordan had just gone out. He would probably be back for lunch at half-past one.

At half past one Teddy was back. He was allowed to wait on a chair in the hall. He waited until just after two, when a brisk, grey-haired lady, whom he had seen up and down the stairs, came to him.

"I'm afraid it's no use your waiting any longer. My husband's just telephoned; he's lunching at the club."

Teddy asked when he could come back.

"You'd better come after dinner, say a quarter-past eight."

Teddy was running no risks of the man nipping out of reach again after dinner. He presented himself at Wilson Avenue (for the fourth time) at eight o'clock. He was alone—Cecil had not returned. Nor had Mr. Jordan. His wife, who opened the door, was looking rather cross.

"He's a bit late sometimes," she said. "I really think you'd better try again later, about nine."

"Please let me wait," Teddy begged. "It's very important—to me."

Mrs. Jordan looked at him, and then said more gently, "You'd better come in here, then."

He was shown into a small room, with a parrot in a cage, a telephone on the wall, and a table littered with papers. The parrot whistled at him, and then said, "Merry Chris". Presently, as an afterthought, it added, "Mass".

After about ten minutes he heard a scraping at the front door lock, then a man's heavy footsteps in the hall. A murmuring followed, a man's voice raised in recrimination, then a swift "Sh-sh!"

Finally the door of the parrot's room was thrown open with some violence. Teddy jumped to his feet, confronting a stout, red-faced man in an unbuttoned overcoat and a bowler.

The red-faced man surveyed Teddy for a few minutes. He seemed to be swaying a little on his legs. Then he said rudely:

"Well, what do you want? You've got a tongue in your head, I suppose?"

Teddy found his voice.

"Please, sir, are you Mr. Jordan?"

The red-faced man seemed to sway more than ever.

"I believe so. People have told me so. Is that all you want to say to me? If so, perhaps you'll allow me to go and have my dinner."

"Please, sir, I'm Edwin Lamb. I don't know—perhaps Mr. Gilbert spoke about me. I was to come back here in three or four years."

He stuck. The man made him nervous.

Mr. Jordan sneered. "Another budding Hayward, I suppose."

"Mr. Gilbert said he'd give me a chance. If you'd let me come up and practise."

"I thought as much." Mr. Jordan leaned forward, took Teddy by the lapel of his coat, and breathed whisky upon him.

"Listen to me, my lad. Every season this club gets applications for a trial from hundreds of youngsters who think they're heaven-sent geniuses. You may be a genius. You may not. From the look of you I should say you're not. You look as if you're just off the farm."

Teddy made no reply.

"Point is, we're full up. No hands wanted. Taking on no more ground staff. Can't afford to. See? You should have applied earlier if you wanted a trial, and in writing, giving particulars. We've quite enough young fellows round the place already, thinking they're second Albert Lambs."

"I'm Albert Lamb's son," Teddy managed to get in.

"Oh, you are, are you?"

Mr. Jordan looked a little disconcerted. He peered a little closer.

"Well, what have you done?"

"Do you mean my cricket, sir?"

"No. Your crochet. Your music. You wouldn't think I'd want to know anything about your cricket, would you?"

"I've been in the country at Burrington. I played for the village last season. Got 61 wickets, average 5.3."

"Village green cricket!" Mr. Jordan showed his teeth in an unfriendly grin. "Think you can step straight from the village green to the County eleven, eh?"

"No, sir. I thought—"

"Let me do the thinking, if you don't mind. *And* the talking. I tell you you're too late this year. And you look too young, anyway. You run along and get into some good club cricket—if you're good enough. If you send in a proper application next year—early, mind—perhaps we'll have a look at you."

"I'm nearly seventeen, sir. If you'd just let me bowl at the nets one morning—"

Mr. Jordan cut him short.

"Certainly. One morning next year. Good evening."

X

CECIL's father had little sympathy with the aspirations of his son's friend. He was not sure that playing games for money was not a species of harlotry, and he had a lurking fear that Cecil might go the same way. But he was touched by the look of misery on the boy's face when he returned, and reported the failure of his mission. "S'pose I'll have to go back to Burrington," Teddy muttered, very near tears. "Cousin Phil won't half laugh."

"I fail to see the necessity for discouragement at present," said Mr. French in his pedantic way. "I believe that this Mr. Jordan is a person of no particular consequence. I understand that he is only acting in a temporary capacity."

"What do you think I should do then, sir?" asked Teddy, not very hopefully.

"Assuming that practice has already commenced, I would recommend you to go to the cricket ground tomorrow, and endeavour to see Mr. Meadows."

"I say, Dad!" Cecil exclaimed. "That's an idea!"

It was, of course, the obvious idea, and should have occurred to one or both of the boys before. Teddy's mind had been running on rails. He had, for years, fixed on the secretary as the proper channel for negotiations, and in his discomfiture at Mr. Gilbert's absence had looked no further than his successor.

Of course, Arthur Meadows was the man! He had captained the County for only two years before Albert's death, but had already endeared himself to the crowd and players alike. Albert had always spoken of him with affectionate respect. He was a man able to exact loyalty and obedience without effort, and although he was not a great player, his enthusiasm for the game, in all its phases, was inexhaustible. Sometimes, in the old days, he would stroll across to where Somerset House was practising during the morning break, and take a boy's bat to demonstrate a stroke, or give a word of advice or praise without a hint of patronage.

Teddy was in a high state of nerves next morning. He had two main worries. First, if Mr. Jordan was on the ground and saw him, would he turn him off? He could only keep his eyes open and hope for the best. Second, what should he wear? To come in full flannels would seem to take too much for granted. He decided on a compromise. He would wear a cricket shirt and a blazer, but the trousers of his dark grey suit, secured by a belt.

Knowing the habits of the players, he did not go down to the ground till eleven. The nets were up, and practice was in full swing. It was a cold, windy morning, with the sun coming and going behind low clouds. Teddy recognised most of the players, Arthur Meadows among them, but the only one to pay any attention to him was Shelly, now one of the leading batsmen of the side, who looked at him curiously once or twice. There were three or four younger fellows whom he did not know, mostly, he supposed, members of the ground staff taken on since he had left Midhampton. They hardly seemed older than himself, and he did not think their bowling looked so good as his own. Perhaps they were batsmen.

After standing behind the nets for a few minutes, Teddy went out on to the field, took off his blazer, and stationed himself where he could stop drives. There were three nets going, and he was kept fairly busy at his self-imposed task, which he shared with two other boys rather younger than himself. He fielded cleanly enough. Once he ran a dozen yards to take a very good catch from a hit by Lemon. Tanner was the bowler, and he called out, "Well held, young 'un," as Teddy self-consciously returned the ball.

At half past twelve Mr. Meadows, who had just finished batting, came across the ground to go to the pavilion. His way took him within a few yards of Teddy, who was suddenly overcome by a sort of paralysis. He made half a movement towards the captain, but his tongue seemed to stick in his mouth. Mr. Meadows caught his eye, smiled, and walked on; but he had not gone three paces before he stopped and turned back.

"Aren't you Baa-Lamb's boy?" he asked.

Teddy was still incapable of speech. He nodded.

"I thought your face was familiar." Mr. Meadows looked at him kindly. He had fair hair, very clear blue eyes, and a large curved nose, giving him the look of an agreeable, rather ridiculous bird.

"Still keen on cricket?" he asked. "I remember seeing you when you were at your prep school. You had quite an idea about bowling."

"I'm awfully keen, sir. I wondered if—"

Mr. Meadows rubbed his nose—a characteristic gesture, suggesting he was conscious of its excessive size, which he thought to reduce by attrition.

"You'd like to have a try, I suppose. Well, why not? No time like the present."

He led the way back to the nets, Teddy following almost incredulously. Mr. Meadows spoke to Lemon, who was about to bowl.

"George, let this young man have your ball for a bit, will you? It's Baa-Lamb's son."

Teddy wished he had not said that. It set a standard of expectation that was not fair to him. It was one thing to be an unknown youngster given a bowl, a youngster who might surprise listless onlookers. It was quite another to be measured by his father's standard. He was aware of eyes turned on him in an interest much too keen for his comfort. The ball felt large and heavy in his hand.

He bowled his first much too fast—sheer nervousness. It was a long hop. Shelly played a merciful stroke, pushing the ball gently into the on-side net. Lemon spoke as he walked back to take his run for the second, "Take it easy. Work up to your natural pace."

Teddy managed to grin, but the words had not reached his brain. He felt his control slipping. Another bad ball would have shattered him. Fortunately he bowled a good one, more by chance than design; a slowish yorker, looking as if it was going to pitch half-volley length, but coming right up. Shelly spotted it only just in time, nearly playing on as he came down hard at the last moment.

"Good one!" Arthur Meadows called out.

All at once Teddy's nerve came back. He was doing something he had done hundreds of times before. He had three familiar stumps to bowl at, and in his hand a ball, which he knew perfectly well what to do with. He had been practising for nearly a month; and there was nothing in it. He set himself to attack Shelly's off-stump with length balls of just above medium pace, turning in an inch or two, but varied by an occasional one which went with the arm. There was no occasion for any more mercy. Shelly was twice beaten without being bowled, and once put up an easy return to a well-disguised slower ball. Only rarely was he able to get his cover-drive to work on one that was a little over-pitched. There was nothing spectacular about Teddy's bowling; what was significant was its normality, that it looked hardly distinguishable in class and certainty from that of the professionals bowling with him.

When Shelly was replaced by Mr. Pearson-Phillips, the

star of last year's Grammar School eleven, Teddy had his reward. He found the edge of the bat several times, and finally lowered the leg stump with a ball that came back five or six inches. "That'll do, old man," said Mr. Meadows presently. "Quite enough for a start."

Teddy put on his blazer. Evidently he was not to be given an innings to-day—perhaps it was just as well, for he knew his batting was nothing like so good as his bowling.

"You did very well," said Mr. Meadows, and then asked him a few questions about himself. "I'd like you to keep on coming up in the mornings for a bit," he said at the end. "I take it you're free?"

"I'm free all right, sir."

"Good. Make it ten-thirty to-morrow, then."

Teddy could hardly wait for Cecil to come home that night. He met him outside Mercer's, earlier than in the old days, and broke the news. Together they examined the implications of Mr. Meadows' invitation to keep on coming up in the mornings. They decided he wouldn't have said that unless he was seriously thinking of taking Teddy on. Obviously, he couldn't have offered an engagement straight away—it was absurd. There were other people to consult, and besides, as far as Mr. Meadows knew, to-day's performance might have been a flash in the pan.

"But I think I bowled well," said Teddy, with guarded optimism. "And some of them were sending down awful piffle. Old Joe Tanner kept on bowling full tosses and half-volleys—I could have swiped them myself."

Cecil was more cautious. "Joe Tanner was always a rotten bowler. Besides, you've been practising; they've only just started." But his caution was in the nature of an insurance premium paid to destiny. He did not believe in tempting providence. In his heart he was almost as exultant as his friend.

Actually, Teddy was kept in suspense just over a week. In that time he got on familiar terms with the players, who called him Ted, and were liberal with encouragement and advice. At this stage, indeed, he felt it would be hard to imagine a more delightful set of fellows. Most of them had known and loved the father, and they vied with each other in showing the son new tricks, until Joe Tanner, the senior professional, protested, "Can't you let the boy alone? Filling his head with all that stuff. You'll make him too big for his boots."

He continued to bowl well, until he became entirely untroubled by any question as to what impression he was making, concentrating on the problem with which each batsmen confronted him. He learned something he had not realised before—that a batsman is an individual, not just a member of the opposing side. Thus a good length to little Plant might be a gift four to Lemon with his long reach; Willis could cut anything the least suspicion short on the off, but was weak in playing a well-pitched up ball on the leg stump, which Joe Tanner (who hardly ever cut) could turn as he liked; Arthur Meadows hated having to play back; and Pearson-Phillips would nearly always mistime a flighted ball.

His own batting disappointed him. He was able to play some nice-looking strokes off the medium-paced bowlers, though he seldom saw runs in them, but Lemon's speed was a little bit too much for him, and he never seemed able to position his feet right for Plant's leg-spinner. He was wise enough not to worry over-much, knowing that everything depended on his bowling.

Now and then he was conscious that people were watching him—old players and big-wigs of the club, like Colonel Thornborough, and Mr. "Batty" Drakes, famous amateur wicket-keeper of a dozen years ago. He sensed that he was being discussed, but the circumstance no longer bothered him—indeed it was rather a stimulus. Once Mr. Jordan appeared, and actually came and spoke to him quite pleasantly; from the way he talked you would have thought Teddy was his own discovery.

On the Saturday week a trial match was played. Teddy was put on Mr. Stokes' side, which batted first, and showing rather scratchy early-season form, were out for 129. Teddy's contribution, at Number Ten, was 5. Then Joe Tanner, after being dropped in the slips, got going. Mr. Stokes and his bowlers toiled away, Teddy (third change) among them, but at the close Mr. Meadows' side had made 237 for 6. Teddy's seven overs had yielded 26 runs without a success, although Buckley was dropped at the wicket off him; and he felt he had little cause for self-congratulation.

But as he was getting his things together, Mr. Meadows came up to him and said:

"Well, Ted, the Committee have decided to take you on, if you want the job. Not much in it at the present, of course—twenty-five bob a week, and maybe some tips. Of course, in a year or two, if you get in the eleven, it'll be more. Are you game?"

Teddy could only say, "Thanks, Mr. Meadows, thanks ever so much."

XI

THE TWO YOUNG MEN decided to celebrate.

Cecil was no longer so keen on religion as he had been. It had been replaced by other sources of excitement. Among these, the Midhampton Hippodrome played a prominent part. It was an old theatre, plain to the point of severity in its external design, but with a resplendent auditorium plenteous in cornice, gilt, and plush. There had been warm controversy at home before Cecil had established a right to pay this resort occasional visits. He won mainly by virtue of a moral imponderable, the fact that he was bigger than his father; also he was handing over three-quarters of his salary, and it was not altogether practicable to deny him control over the remainder.

Cecil indeed had, in a very small way, taken to going out with the lads. Most of these were footballers of the Midhampton Wanderers, who had recently found out about smoking, and beer, and girls, and they broadened Cecil's ideas considerably. Cecil, however, made but a poor lad, cautious about beer, lacking the right air with cigarettes, and prone to mutter an excuse and sheer off when girls loomed on the horizon. What small expertness he had gained in these matters, however, he thought it his duty to pass on to Teddy; and when he was told the good news he said:

"I say, let's go to the second house at the Hippo."

"I say, that's an idea. Who's on?"

"Harry Champion. And Carl Hertz. And some chaps who play footer on bicycles. And a chap called Carmer

Singe or something like that—he pulls a carriage with his eyes."

"With his eyes?"

"He's supposed to."

"Sounds funny."

"I expect it's all right. Shall we go?"

"Yes, rather, let's."

"I've got enough oof this week."

"No—I'll stand treat."

"No—we'll stand each other."

"No—I'll stand it."

"Well. Thanks."

This dialogue took place as they walked from the ground —Cecil had given up a football match to watch the game. Mr. French's polysyllabic protests, when the project was announced at home, were not so much overcome as ignored. It was agreed, however, that they should come "straight back".

They lined up at the Early Doors, threepence extra. Directly the first house was emptied they were let in, and skeltered upstairs to achieve a place in the front row of the gallery. There was a quarter of an hour to wait. They read the local tradesmen's advertisements on the safety curtain, and watched the Late Doors pour into the house, five minutes behind them. The programme was critically discussed, and a dispute arose about the man who was to pull a carriage with his eyes. Cecil supposed this to be a physcial act, however abnormal; Teddy, intemperately imaginative, favoured the view that he used hypnotism.

"Bet you sixpence," Cecil said.

"Bet you a bob," countered Teddy.

"All right. How could he mesmerise a carriage?"

Soon the orchestra plunged into a Sousa march, brief and blaring; powdered footmen changed the numbered cards in their frames each side of the stage; and the curtain rose on the footballing bicyclists. There were only two of them, professing to represent respectively Midhampton Town and Tottenham Hotspurs. They circled the stage, jerking the ball with their front wheels. After being a goal down at half-time, Midhampton rallied to win by two to one—a satisfactory result to the home crowd.

Then there was a soprano, who sang "Love me and the world is mine", a ventriloquist, a "comedy scena", and, just before the interval, Khama Singh, the carriage-puller. Cecil won his bet; it was done somehow with cords attached to the man's eyelids and a small dog-cart, which was wheeled a few yards.

" I say, man," proposed Cecil, as he pocketed his bob, "what about a glass of beer? My treat."

"I don't know."

"It's all right—come on."

"All right, then."

They thrust their way into the bar at the back of the gallery. It was noisy and hot, crowded with pleasure seekers of a humble class. Cecil pushed to the front. He had broad shoulders and a stronger voice than in the days of Garibaldi biscuits, and soon got served.

"How do you like it?" he asked, watching Teddy's tentative sips.

"Not bad. It's not like cider."

"It's not bad beer."

Teddy took a more manful gulp, and emptied the glass.

"Jolly good, really. What about another?"

"I don't mind."

"I'll get it."

Teddy was less successful than Cecil. As he got the beer the crowd was thinning away, and sounds from the auditorium indicated that the curtain was on the point of going up.

"I say, we'll have to hurry."

"No need to hurry. It's only the dancers, we can give them a miss. What about a smoke?" Cecil extended a gun-metal cigarette-case.

They puffed away. It was very worldly, to smoke over their beer, and give the dancers a miss. Teddy began to feel rather dreamy. Cecil's voice came as if from a distance.

"You bowled jolly well, I thought."

"Oh, rot, man. I bowled rottenly."

"I thought you bowled jolly well. *Damn* well."

"Didn't get any wickets."

"Ought to have though—Cadwallader dropping that catch."

"Yes—he ought to have held it."

"He's a rotten wicket-keeper. *Damn* rotten."

"He's a bit slow."

"Do all right for a blind school."

Teddy was visited by a sudden emotional understanding of the generous spirit of his friend. Here was Cecil, filled with joy at another's success, without a thought for himself. He felt an impulse to rival such magnanimity.

"I say, Cecil, why don't you get them to give you a trial?"

"Oh, rot, man. Not good enough."

"Yes, you are. Why don't you try?"

"Besides, there's the office."

"If they took you on you could give up the office. There's your footer too. I bet the Town would take you on."

"If I thought I could."

"Tell you what. I'll speak to Mr. Meadows on Monday. I bet he'd give you a trial if I told him how good you were."

"I say, Teddy. Will you?"

"Of course I will. I'll speak to him on Monday. I promise."

"That's decent of you, old man. *Damn* decent."

"It's nothing. I say, oughtn't we to go back?"

"I suppose we ought. Sounds like the piano chap. Raymond."

The piano chap was soon over. Teddy listened mistily and uncomprehendingly to Harry Champion's quick patter and maxim-gun song effect. No need to give his full attention; he was drawing from a rich well of happiness within. Even Carl Hertz, to whom he had been chiefly looking forward, hardly seemed worth watching closely; one wouldn't be able to see through his tricks anyway. The raising of the lady from the couch, moved him to admiring wonder. Finally half a dozen acrobats flung themselves about swiftly to loud music.

"That's all, isn't it?" asked Teddy.

"Only the Bioscope."

They were shown flickering moving pictures for three minutes. Then they shuffled out. Outside the theatre they met two natty young men with canes, emerging from the pit stalls.

"Hello, Frenchy," called out one. "Pretty poor show, eh?"

"Pretty rotten. Meet my pal, Teddy Lamb. This is Alf Jennings, Teddy."

"How d'you do? This is Freddy Madge."

The young men strolled down the street. Presently Alf Jennings said:

"I suppose we might as well drop into Bobby's."

Cecil answered:

"Well. We ought to go home."

"Why?"

"We ought to go home. It's pretty late."

"It's only ten to eleven. You're only young once, my lad. Come along—be a sport."

"What d'you say, Teddy?"

"Don't mind." He had no notion what or where Bobby's was.

"Oh, well. All right."

They turned into North Street, and entered the saloon bar of a public house. It was almost empty, but a confused babble was audible from the public side. A fair-haired girl, fat and high-coloured, was behind the bar. Her face was redeemed from plainness by an expression of bold good-humour.

Alf Jennings greeted her:

"Well, Gertie. How is the world treating you?"

"It ain't treating me, Mr. Jennings. Not a drink to-night."

"The hint direct, eh? Well, what's it to be?"

They drank port, standing at the bar. Alf Jennings kept up a steady flow of back-chat with the girl. He pretended to read her hand, and predicted a passionate love affair with a dark, handsome young man of twenty-two.

"I believe I can make out the initials," he said. "Yes, I just can—A.J."

"Thought you said 'andsome," retorted Gertie. "The only A.J. I know, he's an ugly little man, with a snub nose. 'E's going bald, too."

"Now then, Gertie—none of your cheek. Or I'll come round and smack your behind for you. I couldn't miss."

Gertie giggled.

"You'll have to come over the bar to do it."

This was a new sort of talk to Teddy. But it was all right. He was a man now—with a man's job. Time he was thinking about girls himself. He had thought of them, of course, but with a sense of shame. But there was nothing to be ashamed of—every man was made the same way.

More was drunk, and the talk grew noisy and boastful. Teddy was feeling extraordinarily happy. This was life. Presently he found himself apart from the others, talking to Gertie with perfect fluency and ease. He told her about the cricket. She seemed enormously impressed—he could not have believed anyone could be so sympathetic.

Presently Gertie said:

"Expect you've got a nice girl waiting for you."

"I haven't got a girl."

"Go on! 'Course you have."

"No, I haven't. You're the first girl I've ever met."

"Don't talk silly."

"It's true."

"You ought to 'ave a nice girl—nice-looking boy like you. You're shy, ain't you?"

"I don't know. P'raps. Don't feel shy with you."

"Ah! That's my experience."

She drew a swift, parenthetical beer for a new customer, and returned.

"How'd you like to see me home to-night?"

"Wouldn't mind."

"Well! You do sweep a girl off her feet!"

"I'm sorry. I meant—I'd like to very much."

"That's better. Well—we have to close soon. I'll be a little time—'bout twenty minutes. I have to help clear up. Tell you what—you wait by the Wellington Memorial."

"All right."

The drinkers were hectored out after a few minutes. Alf Jennings bantered Teddy: "I came, I saw, I conquered. You'd better be careful, my lad. Gertie is hot stuff."

The two young men went their way. Teddy spoke urgently to Cecil.

"I say, Cecil. That girl—Gertie—she asked me to see her home."

Cecil looked awestruck. He rallied with difficulty.

"That's all right. Why don't you?"

"Well, I said I would. But what about getting home?"

"Tell you what, Teddy. I'll wait at the end of the road."

"But won't there be a row?"

"Nothing much. I've been late before. I'll wait for you."

"I say, that's awfully decent of you. I shan't be long."

"No hurry, man."

Teddy started trembling as he waited at the Wellington Memorial. What was he in for? He supposed he would be expected at least to kiss Gertie. He was not sure he liked her so much now he wasn't with her.

Soon she came up to him.

"Hello," she said.

He took her arm awkwardly. "Which way do you go?"

"'Long here."

They plodded along. Teddy found nothing to say, but Gertie did not seem to mind. She was holding his arm rather tightly; he could feel the side of her breast.

"Well," she said, after they had been walking for five minutes, "this is me."

Teddy experienced a sense of failure.

"I suppose we must say good-night," he said.

"Let's see how you say it."

The invitation could not be ignored. He slipped his arm round her waist, put his face close to hers, and kissed her cheek lightly.

"How'll that do?"

"Not bad for a start." She suddenly laughed, pulled him close to her, and pressed his hand hard against her breast. Then she kissed him venemently, on the mouth.

"That'll do for a first lesson," she said. "Come and see me again."

Cecil was waiting at the end of his street.

"Hello, man. You haven't been long."

"It wasn't far," said Teddy.

Mrs. French opened the front door as they were climbing up the steps.

"Come quietly," she said. "Thank goodness, your father's asleep. Cecil, I hope you haven't been leading Edwin into bad company."

"Oh, rot, Ma. Just got talking with some fellows."

They crept up the stairs, to the room where they slept together.

"What was she like, old man?" asked Cecil, as they undressed.

"Not bad." Teddy felt incapable of explaining his very complex emotional condition. "I say. I'm awfully tired. Ready?"

"All right."

Teddy turned out the gas and dived into bed.

"Good-night."

"Good-night."

Teddy believed that he could still just feel the pressure of Gertie's kiss. He lay on his back and contemplated his evening, in high exaltation, before sleep came unexpectedly upon him.

XII

ON THE FOLLOWING Monday Teddy went to work.

He had been instructed to report to Fowler, an elderly professional whose playing days were long over, but who was considered a very good coach. Punctually at nine o'clock Teddy presented himself before this grey-haired, somewhat obese north-countryman.

"Reet, lad," said Fowler. He showed him round the professionals' quarters, explaining the conventions of the place. He gave Teddy the key to a locker, which he was to share with another of the ground boys. "There's a thing or two thou must understand," said Fowler. "You take your orders first from the Secretary, he's the King of England like, and then from the full members, they're the House of Lords. But happen they won't always be here to give you orders. Then thou must do as I tell thee, I'm your boss. And when you're not on a job for me, there's Mr. Goddard. But if Mr. Goddard gives you one order, and I give you the other, I'm the man to obey, see?"

Fowler snapped his mouth shut on the last statement, which was made with more feeling than the rest. Then he took Teddy to the Members' quarters, entering the changing-room. A lot of cricket gear was lying about. Fowler put aside a stack of pads and a dozen pairs of boots. "Take this lot over and clean them 'oop for a beginning. You'll find blanco, and a cloth. Don't put on blanco till mud's brushed off. Dost know to oil a new bat?"

"Yes."

"Tell me how, then."

Teddy explained clearly enough. Fowler cut him short. "That'll do. Take these and do them, when the pads are finished."

Teddy's first morning as a cricketer, then, was passed in brushing and cleaning. It was not quite what he had expected. After he had been at work about half an hour, another boy arrived to help him. This boy's name was Creed, and Teddy had bowled at the same net without getting to know him at all.

He asked Creed, "How long have you been at the job?"

"This is my second year."

"Is there a lot of this sort of work?"

Creed grinned, not without malice.

"It's nearly all this sort of work. You didn't think you were coming to play cricket, did you?"

"I don't know."

"You wait. You'll get an eye-opener before long."

They did not talk too much for the rest of the morning. At one o'clock they went to lunch. In the afternoon Teddy was claimed by Goddard, the groundsman, a morose man with a disconcerting, upward twist to his right eye, perhaps contracted through frequent looks at the weather. He gave Teddy a hand mowing machine and told him to go over an area where new practice wickets were to be prepared—the former ones were getting worn. Afterwards he joined some others in helping to push the heavy roller.

On this first day, he did not touch a cricket ball.

XIII

HIS LIFE settled down to a routine of moderately severe labour. The first County match of the season started on Thursday. It was away from home, and the boys became more in demand at the nets. Most mornings and evenings they practised, in the evenings chiefly bowling to the playing members. This tended to become unalloyed drudgery. Some of the members, particularly the elderly ones, were consequential but very inefficient. One dared not bowl well to them; if one did, they got resentful and angry. Teddy found that most of this class did not really want to improve their batting, all they were out for was some fun at the nets, to have their pet strokes fed; and they were not grateful for bowling which showed up their weaknesses. There were a few really good club-players who went to great pains. Sometimes they put coins on their stumps, sometimes they came to the ground at unusual hours and would call for a couple of boys, who would be taken from whatever work they were at. In these cases there was sometimes a tip at the end—sometimes not. Every now and then Fowler would dispense sums received from the members to the young men, usually two or three shillings each. No one knew how much he kept back; it was one of his perquisites. Nevertheless, he was not unpopular. He kept his eye on the boys, not allowing them to bowl for too long at a stretch, and giving them a little coaching when he had time. He accomplished most of his instruction by demonstration and gesture. He had no use for elaborate theory or advanced technicalities; his cricket vocabulary was homely, almost naïve. But he got his pupils to understand him.

Mostly, however, it was menial work, of the sort Teddy had sampled on his first day; cleaning the gear of members and the senior pros, binding split bats (a difficult art), pushing the rollers about, helping to mark and prepare pitches, including ones for the use of Somerset House. This last was rather a humiliation. His former headmaster caught him at it once, and looked down his nose in discomfort. The son of a well-known and successful pro had passed muster as a pupil, but it was not good to see an Old Boy doing a labourer's job.

The headmaster's unexpressed feeling was that Teddy should either buck up and get famous, or change over to a more genteel occupation. "I hope you've chosen wisely, Lamb," he said. "I confess I'd hoped, with the great advantages your father gave you, you'd find something more suitable."

Things became easier when there was a home county match. There was a little practice early, but when the players came along to loosen up there was not room at the nets for more than one or two of the lesser staff. As the game started boys would be detailed, in turn, to help operate the score-board and, occasionally, if there was anything like a rush, one might be called on to reinforce the two whole-time sellers of score cards. Neither of these jobs was unpleasant if not pursued too long. There was rolling, too, but the rest of the time one could tilt a chair back in the narrow gallery of the pros' quarters and survey the play in a lordly fashion. At such times and such times only—except once, when he was asked for his autograph in mistake for a young Notts player—Teddy was able to feel he was the real thing.

His promise to Cecil was only half redeemed. He knew he had been talking big, and once he started work in earnest he was a little relieved to find that he seldom got near Mr. Meadows. Cecil, with perfect intuitive understanding of the situation, did not broach the subject again, but it was on Teddy's conscience, and after about a week he spoke indirectly to Fowler, who, though blunt in his manner, was quite approachable. He was surprised and relieved to find that Fowler knew something of Cecil's cricket. "Ah, know him—the cross-bat hero," he said. "Tell him to come along to-morrow evening; I'll find time to take a look at him." Cecil was not actually told that Mr. Meadows had delegated Fowler to report on his form, but somehow the impression was conveyed. Cecil begged off early from Mercer's, and scorched into the ground on his new bicycle, a dashing affair of wooden rims, pink tyres, and low-curving handlebars. Unlike Teddy, he was hardly nervous at all. He knew from experience that his eye and muscles hardly ever failed to respond to any demand he made of them.

It seemed, however, to Teddy, who had not seen him play for several years, that his bowling had not come on much. He was quite fast through the air, and steady, if rather short in length, but he seemed unable to do anything with the ball. "Keep thy arm up," Fowler admonished once or twice. Presently he told him to put his pads on. Cecil's batting was lacking in polish, but vigorous and purposeful. It seemed to Teddy that he was giving a very good account of himself. Fowler scolded him constantly. But, "That'll do, lad," he said after about ten minutes. "Go home and practise keeping thy bat straight. Maybe roons'll come more slow, but there'll be more time in the middle for thee to make 'em in. Do as ah tell thee, and happen there'll be room for thee next year." Fowler had already made it clear that there was no chance of the Committee sanctioning another engagement this season, so the form of Cecil's dismissal could be taken as definitely encouraging. "Thy chum's a born hitter," Fowler told Teddy afterwards. "But he's mortal ignorant."

As the season drew on, Teddy got to know his companions better. There were six of them altogether. Highest in prestige were Lumley and Cadwallader, both of whom had played for the county. Lumley was a quiet, efficient, all-round cricketer, rather more intelligent than most of the others. Cadwallader was the reserve wicket-keeper, and hoped to step into Buckley's shoes. He would have to do it on his wicket-keeping, though, for his batting was a joke. The most promising of the younger players was Revill, a most graceful and stylish batsman, who had not yet acquired the knack of making more than 20 or 30 in an innings. He was also a brilliant field, and as for this reason he did most of the "subbing" (often, also, travelling with the team as twelfth man); he was well known to the crowd. He was dark, lithe, and good-looking, and in some danger of getting spoiled. The others were of no particular account—hard-working, unimaginative, utilitarian players who would probably drop out next season.

On most Saturdays there was a club and ground match, generally away from home, against one of the stronger clubs in the county. These were contested with great keenness, alike by the country players, eager to give a good performance against potential county men, and by the amateurs and staff who made up the club and ground side. The latter were competing against each other, and against possible rivals from outside. Lumley nearly always did best both as batsman and bowler, but Teddy and Pearson-Phillips were not far behind with the ball.

On August Bank Holiday and the following day a home match was played against the Middlesex Second Eleven. It was eventually lost by four wickets. Revill made a leap forward with a brilliant 73; Lumley got two useful scores and half a dozen wickets. Teddy surprised himself by making 22 not out in the first innings, and late in the game, when Middlesex looked like getting the 90 odd they required very easily, he caused a shock by taking four cheap wickets. His figures for the match were 5 for 62, and he was able to feel that he had been one of the successes of his most important game to date.

XIV

AS THE SUMMER drew to a close, Teddy began to wonder what to do in the long off season. It was open to him to return to Burrington, but for several reasons he was against this. Most of the other young men had jobs to go to—rather humble jobs, perhaps in the employ of sporting tradesmen ready to submit to the inconvenience of offering seasonal work for the sake of giving young cricketers a leg-up. Teddy, however, had moved in a slightly different social plane, and he did not quite know the ropes.

Late in August Mr. Meadows, to whom he had never mentioned his problem, sought him out and said:

"I've heard of something that might suit you, Ted."

He had referred to the matter at the Conservative Club, and Dr. Littlehampton, who was himself an enthusiastic cricketer, had told him that he could use a boy to deliver medicines. The work would be light, just a matter of cycling round the town two or three times a day, and the doctor could not afford more than ten shillings a week. Teddy thought the prospect rather attractive. Cecil had just taught him to ride a bicycle, and he foresaw a lot of quiet enjoyment in spinning round the Midhampton streets. The difficulty lay in the matter of money; he still had, however, most of his original savings, and had added to them considerably in the course of the cricket season. He decided to accept.

He was still living at the Frenches, and as he saw no prospects of boarding so cheaply anywhere else, he thought it would be imprudent to make a change. Nevertheless, the conditions of the household were beginning to irk him. The excitement of having Cecil constantly in the background had worn off a little, and though neither would confess that they liked the other any the less, some of the glamour of friendship had been lost. Mr. French was sometimes a bore, with his eternal preaching, and he became petulant when little things went wrong. Also, it sometimes occurred to Teddy that he was not getting enough to eat. It was all very well having high tea instead of supper, postulating a solid meal in the middle of the day, but more often than not lunch-time produced nothing more than bread and cheese, with perhaps a little stewed rhubarb. Cecil, who got a good lunch in town, did all right, but Teddy, grown used to a rough plenty at Burrington, was often hungry. Sometimes, when he went out after lunch, he would buy a twopenny milk-cake, or two squares of Fry's chocolate (if you were very hard up you could get a quarter square for a farthing). He felt he ought not to have to do this.

Winter set in. Teddy wheeled and skidded round the town on Dr. Littlehampton's old bicycle; Maisie, Cecil's twelve-year-old sister, caught whooping cough at school; a tremendous battle was fought between rival authorities over a proposed extension of the town boundaries; the headmaster of Somerset House had a heart attack and died; the name of Lloyd George rang through the land. Opportunity knocked at Cecil's door. He was invited to sign amateur forms for Midhampton Town, and from his first appearance with the reserves, played so well that presently, in the absence through injury of a senior player, he was promoted to the Southern League team. Teddy, of course, went to see his first big game, against Brighton and Hove Albion, who were very strong that season. Midhampton were beaten by 2 to 1, but Cecil, at right back, kicking strongly and tackling fearlessly, won his spurs. All at once he became a local celebrity. A career as a professional was open to him, and the two young men thrashed the matter out earnestly and, at length, Teddy was all for seizing the chance at once, but Cecil was more cautious. The final decision was to wait till next year. If, as seemed very likely now his prestige was so enhanced, he was taken on by the county, he would have two strings to his bow, and he could leave Mercer's with an easy conscience.

Teddy was rather at odds with himself during this winter. He was much alone, and for the first time since childhood, he had ample time to think. The nature of his thoughts surprised and sometimes frightened him. He could not have believed it possible for anyone to harbour —nay, cherish—such vile ideas. Surely he was unique in his depravity, it was impossible anyone else could be so wicked. He feared he was going mad. There was no one he could talk to; Cecil and he had always been reticent on the subject. He started going to church, to the elder French's gratified surprise, but he found the services tedious, and unrelated to his problems. The Boy Scout Movement had recently been started, and someone had lent Cecil a copy of Baden-Powell's *Scouting for Boys*. In turning over the pages one evening Teddy lighted on a passage which, though obscure, seemed to come near the point, and next morning he filled the bath with icy cold water, stepped gingerly in, and splashed in agony for a minute or two. *Scouting for Boys* had indicated that he should "jump into" his bath, but he rightly took the jumping to be a mere figure of speech. The remedy made him feel rather sick, and did not produce the right effect. One couldn't go jumping into cold baths half a dozen times a day. He gave it up in less than a week.

He had not gone back to Bobby's since the first night. He had often wanted to, but lacked the courage to go by himself. Cecil would not hear of it these days; since the beginning of his football triumph he had become a fanatical devotee of physical fitness, and believed that a glass of beer would be the ruin of him. Teddy often thought of Gertie, but not seeing her he had to cast round for other divinities. There was a girl in Latter's sweet shop, and one with bare white arms who served in a cabmen's eating house in End Street, and a black-eyed schoolgirl whom he passed every day on his way to the doctor. The only one of these he ever spoke to was the girl at Latter's, but she was business-like over serving and quite unresponsive to Teddy's almost imperceptible advances.

And there was Maisie—who for years had been just a part of Cecil's rather arid domestic background. Maisie had always been very fond of Teddy, none the less so perhaps for the polite indifference with which he treated her. Suddenly she became visible as a remarkably pretty little girl, fair, pig-tailed, brown-eyed, robust like her brother. Teddy decided that he was in love with her. Sometimes his love was very romantic, with fire and water gone through for her sake, and very pure. But this was not always the case.

One day Cecil came back from Mercer's in a boisterous humour, and began to show a side of himself with which Teddy was unfamiliar. It happened that Mr. and Mrs. French had gone to a lecture on Chinese missions, and the three young people were left alone. Cecil began teasing his sister, chasing her, pulling her pig-tails, tickling her. Teddy joined in. A curious half-hysterical mood took possession of both boys. Ostensibly they were just having a rag, but for the first time Teddy apprehended that Cecil was in very much the same boat as himself.

Maisie giggled and struggled. "Don't be a pig, Cecil. Teddy, you *mustn't!*"

Then all at once the game went cold. Maisie settled down peacefully to her homework.

Presently Teddy said:

"Think I'll go out for a bit."

"Want me to come?" Cecil asked.

"Come if you want to," said Teddy.

Cecil looked at him.

"Well, I don't think I will."

Almost to his surprise Gertie was still at the bar. He had two or three beers, and she accepted a port. She seemed delighted to see him, and always came back to him after serving other customers. "I say, Gertie," he said, as she gave him his third beer. "Can I see you home to-night?"

She looked at him with a smile of appraisal.

"Course you can, dearie."

They met by the Wellington Memorial, as before. There was no pretence of seeing her home. She led purposefully to the Waste, behind Victoria Park and an important stage in Teddy's development was reached.

XV

THE NEXT FEW YEARS seemed to pass very swiftly—lively, glamorous years which ever afterwards seem to bear a particular sweetness and poignancy, never recaptured by the post-war world. Events of the moment were going forward, but hardly seemed to disturb the current of the life of those whose places in the social order seemed secure. There was a dock strike and a coal strike. Edward the Peacemaker fell sick and died; George was proclaimed the Fifth outside the Midhampton Town Hall by Mayor and Council in full regalia. Great political battles were fought, culminating in the Parliament Act, and there were two General Elections within a year. Midhampton sent back its two Conservatives, as it had done since 1832, but not without a keener struggle than usual. The brewing interest combined with the Burrington interest to carry the Tory colours home against the Radicals, who had received an access of strength from the new motor industry that was growing so rapidly to the east of the town. Nevertheless, in the country at large the cause was lost, and respectable England had to settle down to resentful obedience to Lloyd George's ridiculous and wicked Stamp-licking Act. "The Insurance Act," they sang in the pantomime at the Grand that year—

"Is now a fact.
You've got to pay
Whatever you say.

You'll get it back
And something more,
When we meet on the beautiful shore."

And Stalls and Circle shouted appreciation of the derisive spirit of the lines.

With the exception of Cadwallader, because Lloyd George was a fellow Welshman, Lemon, who had spent his boyhood in a Nottinghamshire coal mine and was a strong upholder of Trade Unionism, and Lumley, who had worked out a liberal philosophy for himself, the cricketers were mostly staunch but not fanatical Conservatives. There was some chaff when Cadwallader appeared sporting a huge defiant rosette of pale blue and white on Polling Day, but no one seemed to mind much except Mr. Jordan, almost equally assertive in the correct colours, dark blue and yellow. The general feeling was that politics were a dry and difficult business, only becoming exciting when the competitive spirit was introduced at election time. The most important event of 1911 was held to be neither the passing of the Parliament Act, nor the early stages of the militant Votes for Women campaign, but the sensational victory of Warwickshire in the County Championship.

Cecil French joined his friend on the ground staff, easily overcoming his father's opposition. By degrees changes were introduced in the personnel of the County Eleven. Joe Tanner and Willis dropped out, Lumley and Revill achieved regular places. The latter was considered as the most brilliant bat who had ever played for the county; the Press wrote of him as a coming England player. The county passed through a rather successful period, and in 1912 ended seventh, their highest position for a dozen years. It was in this season that both Cecil and Teddy played their first important games.

Cecil was the first. His splendid and tireless fielding had

given him the succession to Revill's old job as twelfth man—Midhampton were ahead of most other counties at the time in travelling with an extra player. One morning at Sheffield, just before play was about to start, Arthur Meadows received a telegram—Mr. Moore, motoring from Derby, had met with a bad accident. He had fractured an arm, there would be no more cricket for him that season. Thus Cecil got his chance, and in a rather disastrous match acquitted himself with credit. After a duck in the first innings he managed to get twenty odd in the second against Hirst, Rhodes, and Haigh. He had played enough Southern League football to lose the novice's fear of a crowd or an occasion, and the reputations of particular bowlers did not intimidate him. He had the gift of playing bowling on its merits.

Mr. Moore, however, was a useful change bowler, and in this respect Cecil did not adequately fill his place. On the few occasions on which he was tried he was expensive. Late in July, on the Saturday morning before the home match with Gloucester, Mr. Meadows came up to Teddy as he was bowling at the nets.

"I've just had the team for Monday pinned up," he said. "You might like to have a look at it when you finish here."

In his excitement Teddy could hardly hold the ball. Cumberbatch clouted two half-volleys into the deep; but presently the nets were pulled up. Teddy rushed to the notice board in the pros' quarters—there was the slip all right, with his name at the bottom of the list. But Cecil's was not there. Cecil himself was putting on his pads; he had been nought not out overnight. When he had finished he came over and congratulated his friend, with a touch of self-consciousness.

"It's a damn shame you shouldn't be in," said Teddy. "Half spoils it for me." But he did not mean this.

Cecil bluffly disclaimed disappointment.

"Can't expect to get a regular place straight away. It's your turn—you ought to have been in before me."

"Oh, rot. Anyway, perhaps you'll get a century to-day, and they'll have to keep you in."

"More likely get a duck."

He did not get a duck, and for a short time looked as if he was in for a big score. But after making 17 very aggressively, he was bowled through hitting across a fast long hop—a fault to which he was still prone.

Teddy got down to the ground early on Monday. The sky was overcast, and the wind blew gustily from the south-west; it looked dangerously like rain. Teddy watched the clock and the sky with anxiety. He changed and went down to the nets. A few of the Gloucester players had arrived, including Jessop. Teddy wondered what the great hitter might be doing to his bowling in a few hours' time. At one of the nets young Randolph was batting—a Wykehamist who had practised early in the season and shown promising form. Teddy realised that his holidays must have started.

Presently Fowler came up and spoke to him.

"Ted, lad, Mr. Meadows wants a word with thee."

Teddy put on his blazer and walked to the centre, where Mr. Meadows was looking at the pitch with Goddard. The captain saw him and came over to meet him. His good-natured face was looking concerned. Teddy instantly divined that he was not to play to-day.

"Well, Ted," said Mr. Meadows. "I'm afraid I've got a disappointment for you."

Teddy assumed the expression of false cheerfulness expected of him.

"I'm not to play, sir?"

"No—the Committee have decided to play Mr. Randolph."

"That's all right, sir."

"Not my fault, Ted—I was outvoted. Never mind—you'll get your chance soon enough."

Would he though? If Randolph was a success, it was not likely that there would be another opportunity this year. Teddy felt cruelly ill-used. It was old Colonel Thornborough who was behind the change, of course, his word was almost law in the club. But he might have at least waited till this match was over. It was not fair to make changes after the team had been posted. Teddy experienced a feeling of real hatred towards young Randolph, with his elegant flannels and cold, arrogant public school face. That was what it was to be a gentleman; other things being even approximately equal, amateurs would always get the preference. Things were made easy for them.

The sympathy of the other professionals afforded him some consolation. They understood his resentment, and with them it was not necessary for him to keep up a mask of sportsmanlike indifference. Cecil, unselfish as ever where Teddy was concerned, was furious; he had by now almost forgotten that it was his own place that had been filled. They could do nothing but abuse Colonel Thornborough and deride young Randolph, and they indulged in these somewhat gloomy pleasures for most of the morning.

Midhampton won the toss and scored briskly until the rain came, soon after lunch. Randolph had not been in, and he did not get an innings; it rained most of Tuesday and Wednesday. He was picked for the next two home games, at Warfield, a large market town in the north of the county, which had recently been given a Cricket Week. Teddy was spared the agony of seeing his supplanter play, but he waited for the scores in a very unchristian frame of mind. Things might have turned out worse. Randolph played four innings with a highest score of 13; it looked as if he was unready for first-class cricket.

There was a blank of three days after the Warfield Week, then came the south-eastern tour, with Sussex, Hampshire, and Kent to be met. The day before they started Teddy was told to pack up and go with the team. Cecil was to go too, reverting to his old position as twelfth man.

XVI

AT BRIGHTON the weather was glorious, and the town crowded with holidaymakers. Young men with straw hats and canes, girls in light summer dresses basked, and paraded, and paddled, and ogled. Donkeys trotted with children on their backs, bath-chairmen pushed invalids about, the little cars of Volk's Electric Railway bumped backwards and forwards between the Palace Pier and Black Rock. Potential cavaliers, vigilant but wary, passed and repassed between the Metropole and the Queen's, where the courtesans walked. A trace of aristocracy lingered round East Street and Castle Square, where an odd-looking Sussex squire in check tweeds could be glimpsed here and there; but democracy ran riot in West Street with generous stenches from Harris's Pork Sausage Restaurant, three cinemas offering continuous programmes, and gross or sentimental picture post-cards on sale every yard or two. Cecil and Teddy, strolling down to the front after arriving in the early afternoon, found the scene enormously stimulating. There was something exciting, boldly erotic about it, and Teddy began to imagine what he could do if he ever got a holiday in this place. But he was on the job now, no distractions that might impair physical effectiveness could be permitted. They went on the West Pier, plied the Gipsy Fortune-Teller with pennies, discovered What the Butler Saw and How Bridget served the Salad Undressed (with some disappointment in each case), tried their strength, and manipulated odd little cricketers in voluminous sweaters but, apparently, no trousers. At half-past ten they got back to their hotel and went to bed.

They found a very different town surrounding the County Ground at Hove—quiet, dignified, spacious. Teddy, a little self-conscious with his cricket-bag, was looked at rather hard by the gatekeeper at the Members' and Players' entrance, but not challenged. As he came down to the ground in his flannels he was beset by two or three small autograph hunters, very insistent that he should sign his name in the right place. At a quarter to twelve the first bell rang, the nets were taken down, and it was learned that Sussex had won the toss. At twelve Teddy came on the field for his first appearance as a county player.

Vine and Robert Relf came out to open for Sussex. Lemon bowled from the north end—strong, purposeful, really fast. His first ball was short, and Vine cut it to right of third man, whence Teddy, running at full speed, cut down a possible four and a likely two to a single. The little round of applause put him on terms with himself.

The score advanced; Vine, slow, somewhat fidgety, looking in greater difficulty than he was, Relf, very elegant and graceful, almost disdainful of the bowling. At 23, however, he played a careless stroke at Lemon, and was bowled. Vine and Killick now settled down to a very sober game. Lumley went on instead of Lemon, and a little later Mr. Stokes, who had been bowling with his usual accuracy for nearly an hour, was replaced by Plant, whose slow right-hand deliveries, pitched well up and breaking from the leg, had Vine in trouble for an over or two. A sharp chance to Cumberbatch at short slip was dropped; then Killick got to Plant's end, and unexpectedly hit a six into the pavilion, scattering a few members.

At a quarter-past one, when Sussex had made 70, Arthur Meadows beckoned Teddy up to the north wicket. Teddy had been kept fairly busy at third man, and fielding singles in the country, and had already made the discovery that first-class cricket feels less awe-inspiring from the middle than it looks from the ring. He was less anxious than he expected, as he arranged his field with Mr. Meadows, but it was nevertheless an ordeal, with the certainty at the back of his mind that people all over the ground, as Number 11 went up on the board, were looking at their score cards and reading his name. There would be remarks, "Lamb? Never heard of him." "He's been playing for Midhampton for years." "No—that's an old fellow; he's retired." "Dead, I believe." "Must be his son." "It's his nephew."

"Don't try anything much the first over, Ted," advised Arthur Meadows. "Just a length."

Teddy realised that the ball was too old for him to move it in the air to any extent. He concentrated on pitching just outside the off stump, allowing his body break to turn the ball on to the wicket. Vine played strictly defensive strokes until the last ball of the over, which was a little over-pitched and went for a single to extra cover.

Plant bowled a maiden over at the other end. Teddy now had to attack Killick, who, as a left-hander, found the ball going away from the bat instead of coming to it. He snicked the first ball rather dangerously through the slips to the boundary. Teddy was now bowling with more venom. The fourth was of the same sort, but it turned an extra inch or so. It just found the edge of the bat, and Buckley took it cleanly. Teddy yelled his appeal exultantly, and the umpire gave him his first wicket without hesitation.

Cartwright came in, another left-hander, with a pronounced crouch and a curious back-lift, in the three distinct stages—body straightened, bat raised to the level of the bails, finally to that of the shoulder. Teddy, over-excited, bowled the first ball too fast and short, and Cartwright cut it wide of third man for two. The last of the over was a yorker on the leg stump—a very good ball. Cartwright came down on it too late and not hard enough. The ball trickled on to the wicket.

The applause was the loudest of the morning. Arthur Meadows came over to pat Teddy on the shoulder; the whole team was delighted at his success.

He bowled one more over, a maiden, to Albert Relf, and then it was lunch-time. Sussex had made 81 for 3, Vine being not out 32.

It was warm work in the afternoon. Vine and Albert Relf got on top of the bowling and were not separated till near the two hundred, when Vine was brilliantly caught by Revill at backward point. After tea, Lemon took the new ball and got three quick wickets, but Vincett, driving hard, and Cox, cutting very cleanly, gave a lot of trouble. Teddy, who had kept the runs down quite successfully for a longish spell during the big stand, came in for severe punishment from Vincett before getting him with a ball that came straight through. The Sussex innings ended for 323. Teddy had taken 3 for 59.

He was a little over-elated that evening. He revealed his mood, not exactly by positive boastfulness, but by a lack of the unobtrusive modesty becoming to a very young player in the company of his elders. He talked, not indeed about himself, but too much. Four or five of the professionals were dining at the hotel, and when, in discussing some of the points of the day's play, Teddy put forward his view a little too didactically, Frank Buckley decided to put in a word. He took him aside after dinner.

"Now look here, Ted," he said, "you bowled very well to-day, and there's no reason why you shouldn't go on doing well if you don't get uppish. But you remember this—most of the Sussex men know our bowling inside and out, they've played against it a score of times. You're new to them, they don't know what's up your sleeve. It's not hard for a young bowler to get wickets before the word goes round about what he can do. You take it from me. You'll have to stomach a mort of hammering before you get anywhere near the top of the tree. You aren't so good a bowler yet as Mr. Stokes or George Lemon or Joe Plant, not by a long chalk."

Teddy was rather dashed, but he recognised the wisdom and real kindness behind the warning. He did his best to bear it in mind next morning, which brought a letter asking for brief biographical particulars from a cricket periodical, a request to pose from a Brighton photographer who specialised in cricket, and a copy of the *Morning Post*, handed him by Mr. Meadows, containing in the account of the game a reference to "Lamb—it is good to see the name in the Midhampton ranks again. A medium-paced bowler with a beautiful action, he got and deserved the wickets of Killick and Mr. Cartwright in his second over—not bad for a beginning."

The rest of the match, however, brought him no particular success. After a second wicket stand between Revill and Shelly, Midhampton collapsed rather badly to Holloway's aggressive fast bowling. Teddy was bowled third ball. But he was given the honour of opening the bowling in the Sussex second innings, Stokes having hurt his hand while batting. He bowled Vine with an in-swinger but got no further wickets. Sussex piled on runs at the expense of a weakened attack, Robert Relf getting a century, and eventually declared at half-past twelve on the third day, nearly 400 ahead. A brave fight to save the game ended in failure just before six. Teddy managed to stay with Plant for twenty minutes. He fluked a four off his first ball from Holloway and afterwards played some nice strokes before an indiscreet attempt to cut Albert Relf ended his innings and the match.

After the game was over he bought a score card with the final score:

SUSSEX

1.	Relf (R.R.), b Lemon	16	run out	135
2.	Vine, c Revill b Lumley	79	b Lamb	4
3.	Killick, c Buckley b Lamb	28	c Meadows b Plant	35
4.	P. Cartwright, b Lamb	2	hit wkt, b Pearson-Phillips	47
5.	Relf (A.E.), c Shelly b Lemon	56	not out	2
6.	H.P. Chaplin (capt.), b Lemon	9		
7.	P.G.H. Fender, b Lemon	2	st Buckley b Plant	29
8.	Vincett, lbw b Lamb	63	b Plant	9
9.	Cox, c and b Stokes	37		
10.	N.J. Holloway, st Buckley b Plant	14		
11.	Street, not out	6		
	B 7, lb 3, nb 1	11	B 11, nb 3, w 1	15
	Total	323	(6 wkts decl'd)	276

Bowling	O.	M.	R.	W.	O.	M.	R.	W.
Lemon	18	3	61	4	9	0	39	0
Stokes	32	12	59	1	–	–	–	–
Lumley	15	6	28	1	22	5	58	0
Plant	29.5	6	94	1	18	3	78	3
Lamb	21	5	59	3	15	4	49	1
Pearson-Phillips	2	0	11	0	6	0	32	1
Cumberbatch					3	1	5	0

MIDHAMPTON

	First innings		Second innings	
1.	Revill, b Vine	84	b Relf (A.E.)	17
2.	Buckley, c Cox b Relf (A.E.)	12	c Fender b Vincett	32
3.	Shelly, c Street b Holloway	64	c Relf (R.) b Vincett	40
4.	Cumberbatch, lbw b Cox	4	b Fender	23
5.	Lumley, b Holloway	7	c and b Cox	55
6.	A.R. Meadows (capt.), c Relf (A.E.) b Holloway	0	b Cox	9
7.	Plant, c Relf (A.E.) b Holloway	2	not out	42
8.	Lemon, c Vine b Vincett	28	b Vincett	1
9.	F.G.Pearson-Phillips, b Holloway	4	b Relf (A.E.)	9
10.	G.L. Stokes, not out	11	lbw b Holloway	1
11.	Lamb (E.W.), b Holloway	0	c Street b Relf (A.E.)	12
	B 4, lb 1, nb 3	8	Lb 5	5
	Total	224		246

Bowling	O.	M.	R.	W.	O.	M.	R.	W.
Holloway	21.4	5	51	6	18	2	63	1
Relf (A.E.)	29	9	54	1	34.2	13	60	3
Relf (R.R.)	5	1	14	0	–	–	–	–
Cox	18	5	56	1	21	6	45	2
Vincett	10	2	22	1	23	5	54	3
Fender	3	0	11	0	6	1	19	1
Vine	5	1	9	1	–	–	–	–
Killick					1	1	0	0

Umpires—Flowers and West.

Result—Sussex won by 129 runs.

Teddy bought a scrap-book next day, and pasted in this card, together with the *Morning Post* clipping, others from the *Midhampton Courier* and the *Sussex Daily News*, and a proof of the photograph, in which he looked very awkward; his arm stretched above his head and his legs together in such a position that it would have been barely possible for him to project the ball twenty-two yards.

He played in the Hampshire and Kent matches and, although he had the satisfaction of getting the wickets of both Philip Mead and Woolley,—his success against left-handers was curious and unexpected—his bowling figures were not impressive. He was less accurate than he had been at Brighton, and twenty minutes furious punishment by E. M. Sprott at Portsmouth did something to impair his confidence. The last two matches of the season were at home, and he was not picked for them. Cecil got his place for the first, and Curtis, a very good club amateur, for the second. Seven wickets for 312, and a batting average of 6.25 was Teddy's not remarkable record for the three games which constituted his first season in big cricket.

XVII

IN NOVEMBER of the same year Aunt Stella died. She had been ailing for a long time, but her end was very sudden. Early one morning Teddy received a wire from Cousin Phil—"Aunt Stella in County Hospital. Condition grave." He hurried to the hospital, gave his name at the gate, and was at once shown into the women's surgical ward. Aunt Stella was almost unrecognisable in her nightdress, with her hair falling lank and thin on her shoulders. She had always been very careful about her appearance, and to expose her like this seemed to be taking an unfair advantage. Her face was of a ghastly yellow colour. She recognised Teddy, and pushed her hand out on the coverlet towards him. He took it in his, sitting down on a chair that had been placed for him. "Make them give me a cup of tea," she said. "I keep on asking." Teddy spoke to the nurse, who answered him briskly. "Sorry, she'll have to wait for the doctor."

Presently the House Surgeon came on his rounds—a red-haired, youngish man with rabbit teeth. He examined her briefly and muttered something to the nurse. "She keeps asking for tea," Teddy heard the nurse say. "Let her have it," said the doctor. "Anything she wants." He moved towards the next bed. Teddy withdrew his hand from his aunt's and went after him. "Please, sir," he said, "can't you tell me something about her? I'm her nephew." The doctor shrugged his shoulders. "It's a perforated duodenal ulcer," he answered. "She was brought too late —I'm afraid there's no hope." As Teddy turned back they were putting screens around Aunt Stella's bed.

She died at five in the afternoon. By then Teddy had heard more about the case from the ward sister and from Cousin Phil, who got in from Burrington by the one o'clock train. A neighbour, calling at her cottage the evening before, had found her desperately ill; the doctor had been summoned and rushed her to Midhampton in his motor. She had never consulted him before. Everyone knew she suffered from severe stomach pains from time to time, but she had always scoffed at the idea of going to a doctor. It looked as if she had been afraid of what a doctor might tell her.

"There'll be summat of money for you," said Cousin Phil, as they left the hospital together, and Teddy thought it would have been in better taste to postpone the announcement. He was stricken with remorse and imbued with a deep sense of what he had wilfully refused to see before, the pathos and loneliness of the latter end of his aunt's life. He knew that she had loved him, in spite of her sharp manner. It would have meant much to her if he had done the sensible thing and gone back to Burrington at the end of each cricket season; if even he had suggested her coming back to town to set-up house with him she would have gladly consented. He had preferred being on his own, had indeed positively neglected her, for he had always cut his rare visits to Burrington as short as possible. He had taken her for granted as a part of the permanent background of his life, and never bothered to show or express any affection for her. Now it was too late.

In a few days it was confirmed that her little income of forty pounds a year, invested in Grainger and Soulby's, the biggest Midhampton linen drapers, was to be his. "You can't do better than keep it in the business," old Grainger told him at the funeral. "I don't know where you'll find a better yield with the same security, and be able to keep an eye on your money like." Teddy was once again slightly shocked at the prompt discussion of the more practical aspects of death, and was short with Mr. Grainger. Nevertheless, when he came to think the matter over it became evident that his economic position was now very much improved, and he was unable to check a little elation. Aunt Stella's money removed the absolute necessity of working in the winter any longer. He had already been considering giving up the job with Dr. Littlehampton ; it was not very dignified for a county player to work as an errand boy.

"I suppose you know what you're about, Ted," said Dr. Littlehampton, when the decision was announced. "I was going to help you to learn something about pharmaceutics. It's just as well to have two strings to your bow."

A month before Teddy would certainly have changed his mind. Now Aunt Stella's money turned the scale. He passed a lazy and unprofitable winter. The ample leisure to which he had looked forward brought him more boredom than happiness. The fact was that he had just enough money to remove the necessity of working, not enough to enjoy idleness. So long as Cecil was available things went fairly well, but early in December Cecil had a stroke of good luck which was a severe blow to Teddy. The older boy, now one of the pillars of Midhampton Town, was transferred at short notice to a northern First Division Club. There was no question of a refusal to go ; making all allowances for the forfeiture of the advantage of living at home, Cecil would be much better off than before. Teddy had been so used to his companionship that he had made no effort to form other close friendships, and for the time being he was left high and dry. Most of his fellow cricketers had their homes in different parts of the county, or if they lived in Midhampton, they were at work ; there was no one for him to go about with. The French household, too, was depressing now Cecil had gone. True, he was better fed now. He got a good dinner for an extra five shillings a week, but it was only inertia and the prospect of Cecil's return in the spring that kept him in the house.

His routine was simple and monotonous. After going for an hour or two's run in the morning on Midhampton Common—an exercise he performed religiously except when the weather was very bad—he would drop into a cinema after dinner, then perhaps spend some time in the new Public Library before returning to the Frenches for high tea. Afterwards he would go for a walk, generally finishing in a bar where he would drink beer till closing time or near it. Sometimes, if he was lucky enough to get into a pleasant company, he drank too much beer. It made him feel stupid and heavy the next morning, and he would make resolutions, but they seemed unimportant the same evening, even if they were recalled at all.

He thought a lot about girls, but had little to do with them. Gertie had become a bad habit against which he fought with varying success, but she had lately got married to a commercial traveller. Her place in his life had not been refilled, and he did not really want to refill it. He felt the need of more sentiment. Gertie had been kind enough, but it had been impossible to idealise her. Maisie might have done, but she was too young ; she thought Teddy silly if he became sentimental. He began to follow young women who attracted him, to make up tales about them, and try to think of ways and means to contrive a meeting. Sometimes, given a hint of encouragement, he found enough nerve to speak, and though he met with one or two rebuffs, his advances were more often met in no unfriendly spirit. They were, however, lacking in expertness; he was too shy, too patently anxious to please, wanting in the proper light touch. Mostly the encounters would yield no more than a little halting conversation petering out to a sudden and final good-bye, and Teddy would tell himself that the girl was not half so pretty as she had looked at a distance. Once or twice indeed, more progress was made, through no initiative of his own, but then it was a half-baked edition of Gertie all over again, usually without Gertie's vulgar warmth and kindness; there was no breath of poetry to dignify the incident.

XVIII

APRIL came round again at last. Cecil returned, looking better dressed and much more sophisticated, the nets went up at the County Ground, days of sunshine poured a benison on the earth. The winter receded as a distant and rather sordid dream, and with the new season there began for Teddy what he afterwards recalled as the happiest and most active period of his life.

A week before the County programme started Gerald

Stokes announced that business would prevent him from playing any serious cricket, except perhaps for a fortnight in August. This meant a vacancy for a medium-paced right hander, the class of bowler which constitutes the most indispensable, if not always the most spectacular element in the attack of a first-class side. Two years ago it would have seemed that Lumley was the man for the job, but Lumley's batting had developed at the expense of his bowling, which, although steady and accurate, was lacking in venom and guile. In the absence of any other aspirant Teddy became the obvious choice for an extended trial. He was picked for the first match, and told that he would not be dropped for at least a month. It was clear that if he did reasonably well he would be given a permanent place.

Teddy realised that he had reached a crucial moment in his career. He might never have an opportunity of recovering ground lost by failure now, might possibly not even be re-engaged next season. He could not claim that things were not made easy for him. There were no odd jobs about the ground now, he was allowed to concentrate entirely on cricket. He practised assiduously, even too zealously, for more than once Arthur Meadows had to tell him to stop bowling. However, his form against his colleagues convinced him that he had only to keep his head and his nerve to make good; and in the practice match, with the conditions helping him slightly, he took several cheap wickets, accomplishing much the best bowling performance of the day.

Nevertheless, the first three matches brought him no particular distinction. But one Saturday afternoon at Edgbaston, when Warwickshire had been set the apparently easy task of making 124 to win, he suddenly got going. The wicket was crumbling slightly, his nerve, brain, and muscles were working in perfect co-ordination, and after bowling Kinneir with his first ball he never looked back. Warwickshire were shot out for 108, and Teddy, bowling throughout the innings, had 7 for 43.

This, as it turned out, was his best performance for the season, but thereafter there was never any question about his place in the team. He played in every match, bowled more overs than any member of the side with the exception of Plant, and took more wickets than anyone except George Lemon—90, at a cost of 21.25 each. His place in the averages was third, properly second, for Cumberbatch, at the head, only bowled in half-a-dozen innings. His batting, too, steadily improved, perhaps the more so because he paid no particular attention to it, and at the end of the season his usual place in the order was nine. His average was only a fraction over eleven, but he often proved, when the occasion demanded it, difficult to dislodge. His best score, 35 not out, made in trying circumstances against Yorkshire, undoubtedly saved his side from defeat.

Altogether, it was a more than satisfactory season, for the county as well as for himself. With their three best bowlers taking nearly 300 wickets between them, Revill, Shelly, and Lumley all finishing with batting averages of over forty, and fieldsmen who held their catches and gave little away, the team was well equipped at every point. One place only was gained in the championship table, but the record was really much better than in the year before, for fixtures with Middlesex and Notts had replaced ones with weaker counties. Revill got a place in the Players' eleven at Lords, and, next March, his portrait in Wisden; George Lemon was picked for the Rest of England against the Champion County; and Shelly made local history by hitting two centuries in the home game against Worcestershire—a feat that had never before been accomplished for the County.

To Teddy, the summer brought more than cricket success, though it may be said that the richer life he began to lead was made possible only by his new position as a person of some consequence. With a regular fee for each county match, and the prospect of talent money at the end of the season, he was far better off than he had been before. It was a perpetual delight to him to visit strange towns, and to see for the first time famous cricket grounds that had hitherto been only names to him. The metropolitan excitement of London, the grim industrialism of Sheffield and Manchester, the pastoral delight of Tunbridge Wells and more particularly Horsham, each appealed to his romanticism in a different way, each seemed to impart an unmistakable local flavour to the cricket played there. You were a little anxious and very correct at Lords, you would hardly dare, unless you were George Hirst or David Denton, to take the liberty of hitting a six at Bramall Lane, at Horsham it didn't really matter whether you won or lost, you just did your best to have some fun.

But it was the companionship that counted more than anything. Under Arthur Meadows, Midhampton was a very happy side. It was not only that he was a very good captain on the field; he had a real affection for the men who played under him, an affection that was warmly reciprocated. Though his outlook was simple, essentially feudal in fact, he never gave an order in a brusque or peremptory fashion; he hardly ever seemed to give an order at all. He had a sympathetic insight into people's states of mind which transcended mere cleverness, knowing by intuition when to encourage, congratulate, or console, always unobtrusively, with no parade of tact. He made no attempt to direct the players' lives off the field, but his own keenness and high standard of physical fitness set an example which, with occasional lapses, everyone was glad to follow. As a player he was not remarkable, seldom rising above the class of a stylish club batsman not quite up to County standard. But he had days of success, and this year he managed to get his first century, after a dozen years of first-class cricket, against a rather weak Somerset attack. The applause when he reached his hundred was tremendous, and a very substantial contribution, both in volume and length, came from the professionals' gallery, whose occupants stood up and cheered themselves hoarse.

Freddy Pearson-Phillips and Godfrey Moore were the only other amateurs to play regularly. Moore was a hard-working all-rounder, with a pleasant but rather colourless personality. He drank heavily, but never seemed the worse, nor in any way different, for drinking. Pearson-Phillips, a very tall young man with a lot of heavily creamed dark hair and a somewhat supercilious manner, was not altogether popular. He held himself rather aloof, and was suspected of conceit. He was, however, a useful fastish bowler, taking full advantage of his height, a dangerous hitter when in the vein, and a fine outfield. The chief thing noticed about him off the field was his enormous red "Indian" motor cycle. He generally had a girl in the side-car, but not often the same one twice running.

Buckley, Cumberbatch, Plant and Lemon were the senior professionals. Buckley, the wicket-keeper and a useful opening batsman, was forty-five, and this was his last season. He was a stout, moustached, blunt man with the look, and generally the taciturnity of a head gardener. Cumberbatch was a left-handed batsman for whom a great future had once been predicted, but who had never quite come up to expectations. He neither smoked nor drank, but his temper was a little uncertain, and when he was in a bad mood it paid to avoid him. Joe Plant was the " card " of the team, as befits a slow bowler of small stature. He was very good-natured, and did not fall into the error of taking his cricket with too great solemnity. He was, in fact, quite incorrigible on the field, and his bowling was a kind of trick monologue. More than once he had been known to break up an obstinate stand by making a batsman helpless with laughter, and there would be hard feelings, but it was impossible to be angry with him for long. He was thirty-five, two years older than George Lemon, a fast bowler of the old school, of splendid physique, tireless energy, and real speed. Again like the older sort of fast bowler, he was a mighty hitter and absolutely fearless in the field, catching and stopping drives at mid-off almost before anyone had seen them. He was a simple, kindly soul, and a famous beer drinker, getting rather embarrassingly affectionate when in liquor.

Nearer to Teddy's age were Shelly, Revill, and Lumley, and the four of them, with Cecil—who got an occasional match but still was generally twelfth man—formed a little group apart from the rest. Shelly was the oldest, a hard-driving, fast-footed batsman, rather inelegant but very effective. He still looked the same freckled, light-hearted youth who had tried to intercept Teddy on the day of Baa-Lamb's collapse. He did not appear to be at all clever, but he had an unexpected passion for classical music, playing the violin for the Midhampton Symphonic Society's Orchestra. Lumley was an excellent sort of young man—intelligent, well-mannered and self-controlled. He was a Unitarian, and had thoughts of training for the ministry of that body. Teddy—"Ewe-Lamb" as they called him, in reference to his initials and in recollection of his father's nickname—conceived a great admiration for Lumley, and felt honoured by his friendship. It was, however, Jim Revill who had the bigger immediate effect on his way of life.

Revill represented something at that time rather

unusual in the game. To call him a gentleman pro would have been, in the light of approved definitions, perhaps an exaggeration; Colonel Thornborough would certainly not have allowed him a title to gentry. But he was clearly a grade or so higher in the social scale than his colleagues, of the same class, let us say, as Freddy Pearson-Phillips. He had been to the Grammar School, but had made no scholastic headway there, not from lack of ability but owing to a sort of amiable worthlessness, a technique of charm enabling him to evade all penalties for neglected work. He was that rare phenomenon, a born cricketer. Where he got it from was a mystery, for neither his father nor his grandfather, both fairly successful dentists in Midhampton, had ever shown the slightest interest in the game. Yet, without any instruction, he was discovered to be positioning himself correctly from the first moment he was given a bat to play with, and at the Grammar School his performances were so brilliant, his lack of any other exploitable talent so manifest, that he was allowed to join the ground staff with hardly any parental opposition.

He was exceptionally good-looking, and not unduly modest. There had been a time when he looked like getting spoiled, but he had shown good sense enough to profit by a few rebuffs, and was now very easy to get on with. He conceived a fancy for Teddy, showing a willingness to take him in hand, and Teddy, although actually a few months the older of the two, gladly accepted a position of tutelage. The points on which he was instructed related to fashion, taste, women, manners and social behaviour generally. In particular Jim was very decided in the matter of clothes. He pointed out, without mincing words, the ugly shapelessness of Teddy's suits, the incongruity of his ties and socks, the vulgarity of his boots. Soon he had him wearing carefully chosen straw hats, blossoming ties, secured by elegant pins, and suits made to measure, with tight waisted jackets and narrow trousers firmly creased, not too long to prevent, when seated with legs correctly crossed, a view of heliotrope socks over the highly polished brown shoes.

It was, it will be remembered, the age of the "nut". It was a curious type, with physical characteristics almost as strongly marked as sartorial ones. Pale young exquisites, short and slim, with vacuous oval faces and names like Algy or Reggie or Archie were to be found everywhere. Further external signs were a quantity of hair, liberally oiled and brushed right back without a parting; the easy manipulation of canes, monocles, cigarettes; and a talent, according to temperament, either for cold pride or lively chatter about nothing in particular. It was seldom one got all these features combined in one person; then indeed one got that fine flower, the Knut with the "K"; but the tradition affected nearly all young men except the most loutish; and there were many good points about it. Though it ran the whole gamut of the social scale, it was by origin aristocratic, and demanded a certain standard of manners. It militated against the cruder forms of boorishness, and this showed itself particularly in the matter of the pursuit of women, one of the major preoccupations of the tribe. Advances were made in a more gallant and delicate manner than heretofore, a pick-up on Brighton front could be given an atmosphere of chivalry, almost of poetry.

Most nuts were inclined to be weedy, shunning vigorous exercises or rough sports, but there was a substantial athletic minority which really had the pull over its hothouse brethren, so long as it cultivated the correct repose and brought no too direct hint of athleticism into society. Of this sort Freddy Pearson-Phillips was a very fair representative. Jim Revill was by no means a slave to nuthood. His taste, if a little flamboyant, was fundamentally sound, and protected him from the excesses which carried the movement into the region of ridicule. This circumstance, combined with his good looks and rising reputation, made him enormously successful with women; really too successful for much of the joy of pursuit and siege was lost in the absence of genuine resistance.

"Make 'em come to you, my lad," he said to Teddy once. They were leaning against the rail of the esplanade at Southsea, and he was referring particularly to seaside technique. "Just one look to show you like 'em, then wait till they come back. They will, nine times out of ten. Then if you get a proper glad-eye, go in and win."

Yes, ruminated Teddy, fingering the beginnings of his moustache, perhaps that was all right for Jim, but if *he* was to wait for them to come back he might have to stay there till Doomsday. He was, at twenty, less good-looking than at one time seemed likely. His face was pleasant and intelligent, but it lacked distinctive character, the eye did not rest on it. His diffident manner was also against him. Jim Revill put himself to great pains to get his friend off in the different towns they visited, and could not understand why the encounters he contrived ended so disappointingly. He had very little imagination, and though, of course, Ewe Lamb (or Yule, as he abbreviated it) had not his own advantages, it seemed to him absurd that he could not get along well enough.

"Getting them's easy enough," he said. "Shaking them off's the real job."

At Newborough, where he was unexpectedly given his first taste of Festival Cricket in September, Teddy did better. The Newborough Festival, under the patronage of a local nobleman, was the most enjoyable of the events of its kind, and an invitation to play at the famous

Yorkshire seaside resort meant not only a compliment to one's cricket, but a promise of a delightful time. Revill had been picked for all three matches, for the M.C.C. v. Yorkshire, for the South against the North, and the Players against the Gentlemen. A famous bowler slipped on a hotel staircase the day before the first of these games, and Teddy was wired for. He packed up in high glee, and after a long night journey was met at the station next morning by Jim Revill, who welcomed him with the words:

"You're lucky all right, Yule. This is a great place. Hundreds of girls. You can't help getting off."

Teddy was to play in the first two matches. He got a few wickets, and to his great surprise hit up fifty odd against the North, but the match was set for a draw and the best bowlers were being rested. Most of the evenings he spent looking for girls with Jim; and indeed, they were easy enough to find, far easier than at Southsea, where they had been too early in the season. Teddy's technique began to improve. He found the Yorkshire girls more direct, less self-conscious than those of the South; they made his shyness seem of less consequence, and often broke it down altogether. The encounters were not, however, quite satisfactory. He and Jim went hunting in pairs, and it was an unwritten law that only pairs should be tackled; in fact, very few solitary girls were to be seen. But it nearly always turned out that there was one pretty and one plain girl, and by a process of natural selection Teddy nearly always got the plain one. Except on a single occasion, when the pretty girl showed such a decided preference for Teddy that she could not be gainsaid. Jim was annoyed for a moment, but was quickly able to accept the situation good-humouredly. Teddy was rather damped when his prize hinted a reason for her selection of him:—"Your friend's got too much conceit of himself;

he wants taking down a peg or two." This affair ended tamely enough, in a few kisses and a little fumbling. Most of the passages were like that, but once Jim, whose judgment was generally so sure, made a mistake. The two young men were led purposefully up the Castle Hill, confronted, when it was too late, with a demand for money, and then dealt with swiftly and thoroughly. "I made a bloomer that time, old man," admitted Jim sheepishly afterwards, when they met, according to their usual arrangement, at the familiar station under the cliff. "You take my advice, and keep off the tarts, unless you've no chance of getting anything else." He proceeded to give Teddy clinical advice applicable to such contingencies.

Altogether, Teddy felt in every sense much more of a man after his first full season. He had money in his pocket, good clothes on his back, new friends. In October he moved to a boarding house in Albert Square. Cecil, who had been much less exclusively his friend during the summer, had, of course, returned to Liverpool at the end of August, and the prospect of another winter with the older Frenches was not attractive. He now had plenty of company and no temptation to drink in bars; under the influence of Lumley, he began to read to some purpose, and rediscovered a long smothered interest in History; and he enjoyed a not very strenuous love affair with the daughter of the house. Though it was decorous and romantic, it taught him much about women's moods and responses, but he was at no moment able to feel involved in anything fundamental. Finally, however, the girl began to get possessive, and Teddy was brought to realise, with more discomfort than pride, the truth behind Jim Revill's warning of the difficulty of "shaking them off". He welcomed the coming of the new season as giving him a chance of getting away, and fortunately the girl got a job in London in June. She wrote him a few sentimental letters, rather succinctly answered, and then faded out of his life.

The season of 1914 brought him increased success. He was called on for a great deal of work, as George Lemon developed trouble with his left foot, and was out of the game for two long periods. This misfortune was reflected in the County's record, which was much less impressive, but Teddy at least had no cause for discouragement. At the end of July he had already taken over a hundred wickets, a little more cheaply than had been the case with his full record the year before. He was thoroughly happy. He had youth, health; and perhaps real fame was just ahead. A vista of golden years—twenty, twenty-five, thirty of them perhaps, stretched before him.

XIX

ONE SUNNY AFTERNOON in late August, Midhampton, engaged in their last home match of the season, were confronted with the difficult but interesting task of getting 303 runs to win in four hours. After two wickets had gone for less than 30, Shelly and Cumberbatch settled down to bat with great resolution, and though they were some little way behind the clock a victory for the County began to look a possibility.

Just after four o'clock a sound of brassy music was heard, and presently a company of khaki-clad soldiers, headed by a regimental band, appeared in the ground. Passing through a gap at the south end, where the heavy roller stood, the soldiers unexpectedly marched right on to the playing pitch, paying no attention to the cricketers, who had to move out of the way. Orders were barked, platoons formed, drill manœuvres executed. The players watched the performances for a few minutes, looking rather sheepish. Then, as the umpires pulled up the stumps, they trooped off. It was the last of county cricket in Midhampton for nearly five years.

In this fashion did the coming of the Great War first really impinge on Teddy's consciousness. Previously it had seemed a political stir of more than usual excitement and violence, but of no special concern to himself. Though Colonel Thornborough had come out strongly in favour of stopping all cricket, most of the professionals, with a personal interest in the shape of match fees, had considered the suggestion silly and panicky. It was incredible that the Kaiser really intended to defy the combined might of Britain, France and Russia, and, when it became fatally clear that he did, equally incredible that he could hold out more than a month or two. It was true that Lumley, who studied the strategical articles in the newspapers, took a less confident view. "It looks like a race," he said. "A race between von Kluck and the Grand Duke Nicholas. If the Russians get to Berlin first the war'll be over at once. But if the Germans get to Paris first, it may last a year or more." This theory, however, won little credit. Lumley was clever, and clever people were notoriously always wrong. No one could seriously suppose the Germans capable of getting to Paris; look how the little Belgian army had held them up. Now that General French was going out to help General Joffre, the idea was preposterous.

There was a little time to go before uneasy young men were to be outfaced by Kitchener's glassy stare from every hoarding. Comparisons with the South African War were still possible, and Teddy, just able to recollect that struggle as stirring and heroic matter for newspaper reading and boys' serials, recalled also that it had not made the slightest difference to his own life or that of anyone he knew. War was a matter for soldiers and sailors, who were, after all, paid to defend their country, and were cheered and feted when the time came for them to do so. One had heard of conscription in continental states, but England was a free country and would never stand for that sort of thing. Her Regular Army had proved time and again that one volunteer was worth ten pressed men, and that she could never be overcome by hordes who had to be practically driven into battle. Napoleon had tried it, and where he had failed was it likely that the ridiculous, swaggering Wilhelm, with his theatrical cloaks, jack-boots, spiked helmets and upturned moustaches, could succeed? "Leave it to K." was the phrase of the day—and then it suddenly appeared that K. did not share the view that the winning of the war was exclusively his job.

The first significant incident was the return from Liverpool of Cecil French, a day or two after the first appeal for men. He came to see Teddy in his boarding house, and announced his intentions without preamble.

"Thought I'd join the Army," he said. "What about you?"

Teddy looked puzzled and worried.

"But it's not your job, Cecil," he expostulated. "And you haven't had any training."

"Soon get that."

"Supposing you get killed?"

"There was a man up at Liverpool—a sergeant he was—told me that only a few get killed."

He was going round to the Recruiting Office of the East Midhamptons next day. Nothing could shake his determination. He had thought he would prefer to be with his own lot, that was why he had not joined up in Liverpool. Besides, his idea was Teddy might go along with him; if they were together they would have some fine times.

But Teddy could not make the adjustment so quickly; it seemed to him that Cecil was doing a foolish thing. He had more imagination than Cecil, and the idea of being killed or painfully wounded rather appalled him. It must be recalled that the great drive of public opinion in favour of sending all able-bodied young single men to the front had not developed immediately. There was a good deal of not very vocal resistance to the idea that the Regular Forces could need the help of trained civilians. If one withstood these strange new exhortations to join up, one could still do so in good company.

Cecil duly went along to the Recruiting Office, was passed medically fit, and was soon off to camp at Modsham. A few days later Mr. Meadows called on Teddy. He was in a captain's uniform; he had held a commission in the Territorials for many years.

"Well, Ewe Lamb," he said, when they were alone in the little alcove reserved for the reception of guests' visitors. "I've really looked in to say good-bye. I'm off to Bulford to-morrow."

"Where's that, sir?" asked Teddy, politely.

"Wiltshire, I think. Not far from Salisbury Plain."

He seemed shy and embarrassed. He offered Teddy a cigarette, and talked trivialities for a few moments. Then he said:

"I'm trying to see all the fellows before I go. They're not all here, of course. I was sorry to miss French. Did you hear that George Lemon has joined up?"

"No, I hadn't heard," answered Teddy, innocently. "I hadn't seen him around—but then I wouldn't expect to, as he doesn't live in town."

"Jack Lumley's going too. And Bob Shelly, I believe." He paused and pulled at his cigarette.

"I wondered if you had thought about it yourself," he said presently, with an air of casualness.

Teddy felt himself blushing.

"I don't know," he replied. "It's not going to last very long, is it, sir?"

"One never knows. The feeling now seems to be that it may be a bigger job than we all thought at first. I believe we need men pretty badly."

Both were now extremely self-conscious.

"Perhaps you're right, sir," Teddy said. "I'll think about it seriously."

"I wish you would, old man. I'm sure you won't regret it."

Regret what? Thinking about it? Or joining the Army? A little ambiguous!

Captain Meadows held out his hand.

"Well, I must be off now—got some other fellows to see. Good-bye, Ewe Lamb, and best of luck whatever happens."

"The same to you, sir."

Teddy was rather disturbed by the incident, and for the first time began to think of enlistment as a serious possibility. If Jack Lumley was going, there must be something in it. Nevertheless, he hesitated, and finally let things drift on. He rationalised his unwillingness by arguing that it simply wasn't worth while going when everybody said it would be over by Christmas—except Lord Kitchener, and he had an axe to grind. Why run the risk of getting killed or crippled, and in any case submit to the grim rigours and discipline of military life, when it was clear that the Germans couldn't possibly hold out much longer? If there was any danger of losing the war it would be a different matter. But you had only to read the papers, *John Bull* and the others, to realise how absurd that was.

He did not give in until well into the New Year. It was

the bombardment of Newborough that started his debacle. He *knew* Newborough, this was really bringing the war to his own door-step. There was a Hasleden cartoon in the *Daily Mirror*, depicting the harvest of Newborough as a multitude of uniformed recruits, a swarm of hornets winging through the air to sting and madden the cowering Kaiser who had disturbed their nest. The following day Teddy, turning over a newspaper in the Public Library, had a white feather swiftly and expertly pinned on his jacket by a flapper of sixteen. He took the thing out, burning with resentful anger, conscious of derisive eyes that had witnessed the incident. "Silly little bitch," he muttered. "Oughtn't to have been let out of the nursery." He was damned if he knew he was going to be intimidated by goads of this kind. But the imputation of cowardice rankled. He spent a wakeful night telling himself he wasn't afraid, it was simply that he had too much sense. The next morning he sullenly presented himself at the Recruiting Office.

XX

TEDDY never saw the Western Front. His military career may be summed up as a series of mischances which perhaps saved him from death or disablement. He had not been training for more than three weeks when he was shot in the right foot at musketry practice owing to the carelessness of some fool. The wound proved troublesome; he was still unable to move when the battalion was drafted to France, and presently he was transferred to a London Hospital. Here he got better quickly, and before being discharged was given a fair amount of liberty; it was pleasant to move about the West End in hospital blue, and receive the same sympathy and kindness as real wounded soldiers. Soon, after a brief leave, he was back in camp again in a different unit; and became, after a little while, the victim of another accident, this time with four others, who were sent into the gas chamber with defective respirators. Getting over the effects proved a painful business, but another French draft was dodged, and Teddy only saw active service, comparatively late in the war, at Salonika. Here he had a little fighting, mostly scrambles for mountains. He may or may not have shot a few Bulgars, and presently the order of evacuation came. On the troopship on the way home, practically everyone fell victim to malaria; in Greece they had been regularly dosed with prophylactic quinine, which was now stopped, so that the suppressed fever was able to come out.

The rest of Teddy's war was spent in England. He was promoted Corporal for no apparent reason except length of service, mostly in hospital, and the Armistice found him helping to train boys of eighteen, in the Eastern Command. It could not be said that his experiences as a soldier were either severe or glorious, but he had been miserable most of the time, and had latterly developed a gloomy belief that the war was never going to end. Right up to November, 1918, he persisted in this, having learned from many bitter disillusionments that the appearance of success was too often the prelude to disappointment and despair. The news of the Kaiser's abdication he received with incredulity, and even when the matter was past all doubt, the war was really won, he suspected some catch. He was not alone in fearing, for two or three years longer, that somehow the whole thing might break out again at any moment.

His health, of course, was not good, and this may have

added to his depression. He had a severe bout of the "Spanish flu". His malaria seemed to be always coming back on him, and, like almost everyone in Europe in varying degrees during the last year of the war, he was suffering from the effects of bad and insufficient food. He longed to get out of the Army, but because his occupation was one of no importance to society he was passed over in batch after batch. For a time it looked as if he would be sent to the Rhineland with the Army of Occupation, but he managed to escape that, and was eventually demobilised in June, 1919, just before the signing of the Peace of Versailles.

He was one of the lucky ones. Of the Midhampton Eleven of 1914, nearly all of whom had been drawn into the vortex of war, heavy toll had been taken.

Freddy Pearson-Phillips had lost a leg. He had joined the Royal Flying Corps, where he had a longer run and an easier finish than most. His hair, as sleek and thick as ever, had turned quite grey, and he made an impressive figure as he skilfully steered his invalid's motor chair through the streets of the town. He had ended as a Major, and drew a good pension, most of which went on whisky.

Godfrey Moore was killed, and Cadwallader blinded. Lee Cumberbatch, who had a large family and never wanted to go, had been netted at last when conscription came in. He was badly wounded and taken prisoner in March, 1918. The German surgeons did their best for him, but he could not be given enough food and he never recovered his strength. He died a few months after his release.

Cecil French had been dead nearly four years.

Teddy only met him once after his enlistment. It was in London. He was recovering from the wound in his foot. Cecil had seven days' leave from France. He spent it in Midhampton, but came up to town on the morning of his last day. His train left Victoria at six, and he met Teddy for tea at the Coventry Street Corner House. He was a Lance-Corporal. He looked in magnificent health; one would have said he was thriving on the war, but Teddy found him more than usually quiet. "It's all right," was practically all he would reply to questions about the front with which Teddy, painfully aware that his own turn was likely to come soon, plied him. The only subject he discussed with any animation was sport; they went over, in minute detail, cricket matches in which they had played together, for the County, or further back at Somerset House. But near the very end, as the bus taking them to the station wheeled by the Winged Victory at Hyde Park Corner, he announced abruptly: "Going to get married next leave." He had fallen in love with the daughter of the family with which he had been billeted at Modsham the previous winter. They were to have been married this leave, but the girl's father had just died. "She knows about you," said Cecil. "I'll give you her address—you must look her up on your sick leave. It's not far from home."

Soon he was swallowed up in the frantic hectoring bustle of a Victoria that seemed all khaki. "Don't forget to look up Milly," was the last thing he said. Teddy limped on to a bus which took him to Camberwell. He never looked up Milly. He spent his leave in London; there was nothing to take him back to his native town. A few months later, just after he was gassed, a letter from Cecil's mother reached him. Cecil had been posted as "Missing, believed killed." It appeared there was no hope. The letter was written in a mood of pitiful, almost hysterical Christian resignation. Teddy was too desperately ill to feel the full force of the blow, and by the time he was better the shock was deadened. Nevertheless, he was deeply affected by Cecil's death, which added poignancy to the dull misery of these years of desolation. There was, literally, no one left for him to care for. It would be better to get himself killed out of hand. He tormented himself with remorseful recollections of how he had neglected his friend during that last happy summer. Cecil had never cared for going after girls, and more than once Teddy had made excuses not to go out with him, so as to follow up his fascinating new preoccupation in the company of Jim Revill.

Jim had come through well. He joined up a little later than Teddy, and after he had spent a few weeks in the front line, wires were pulled. The Colonel of his battalion was a great cricket lover, and it did not seem good to him that the life of a potential England batsman should be risked unnecessarily. Jim was sent home for training in an Officers Cadet Battalion, was presently given a commission, and thereafter never left the Base. He finished as a Captain, splendidly tailored, more handsome than ever, and without a scratch.

Arthur Meadows got through. He spent most of the war in the East, and was with Allenby when he entered Jerusalem. Lumley, like Revill, got a commission from the ranks, and escaped with a slight gassing. George Lemon acquired a Distinguished Conduct Medal, the rank of Sergeant, and two wound stripes; neither of the wounds, however, was very serious. Joe Plant, in his own cunning way, succeeded in dodging the bullets. Shelly got into the Navy. His first ship struck a mine; he was one of the very few to be picked up, after spending fourteen hours in the water. He was little the worse for the experience and had no further mishap.

XXI

ALMOST EVERYTHING after the war, it may be remembered, was expected to be bright. At a time when the tone of society was set by young persons who practised games like Beaver, indulged in small hour treasure hunts in public places, and swarmed to parties to which they had not been invited, almost everything was forgivable except dullness. The war had been a colossal bore; it was *tabu* as a subject for books, plays or even conversation; and it had been fought in vain if it had not made the world safe from boredom.

Among the many things of which brightness was demanded, cricket took a prominent place. The spirit of the times, it was argued, was against the stylised leisure of the old days. Batsmen must get on or get out; they should be penalised for playing out maiden overs, and returned in disgrace to the pavilion after a certain number of them. Left-handers ought to be abolished; they wasted time. Innings should be confined to a time limit; the side which made the most in the time was the winner, never mind how many wickets fell. No county should be allowed to play more than five professionals. The County Championship should be recognised on the same basis as the Football League, with two divisions, promotion and relegation, and no points allowed for drawn matches. Unless, in fact, the game put its house in order, made itself acceptable as an entertainment to a generation requiring violent stimulants, it was done, it would be replaced by baseball.

The authorities prudently disregarded the greater part of the advice they were offered, but made one important concession. Matches were to be restricted to two days, with considerably extended hours of play. The aim was twofold; to compel quicker scoring, and to enable the man who was at work all day to see a little cricket in the evening. Neither object was achieved. There were as many complaints of slow batting as ever, and the tired worker, in general, preferred his home and his tea to the off-chance of sixes between half-past five and half-past seven. After one curious and unsatisfactory season, the experiment was abandoned.

When Teddy returned to Midhampton, the season was nearly half spent. He found the atmosphere much changed. He was no longer a promising youngster; he was an experienced player, one of the old brigade round whom a new team had to be built up. He was only twenty-six. It was startling to find Arthur Meadows, Plant and Lemon the only regular players of longer service than himself; the rest were either contemporaries or juniors. Another surprise he was soon to get was the low standard of the cricket. At times it hardly rose above that of club and ground matches in the old days. Death, disablement, and advancing years had removed almost half the old hands, and there was nobody much to take their places; there was, in fact, an acute shortage of cricketers. Ex-officers who had not been good enough for their first elevens at school were suffered to disport themselves on county grounds, smiting blithely away with their cross bats and getting a few wickets with their long hops; players who had dropped out before 1914 were given a second chance; and club bats like Dr. Littlehampton, who, at the age of forty-three, was able to realise a life's ambition by getting a few games for the County, all helped to swell the long list of men tried in this odd year.

It was the bowling that was particularly bad. Experienced batsmen were able to get back in the way of run-getting after hard practice, but it took longer for a bowler to work off the stiffness engendered by four years' absence from the game. In consequence, it was easier to make runs than it ever had been before, and it was only the mediocrity of the batsmen who were called on to fill the ranks that prevented a crop of mammoth scores. As it was, the Tens and Elevens of the old days began to get ideas. Joe Plant was given the task of opening the innings; and before July was out Arthur Meadows had hit three hundreds.

It might have been thought Teddy would profit by this state of affairs. Actually he had a disappointing, even a disquieting half-season. He was not fit, and found the new long hours exhausting. Standing about in the field was an ordeal, and bowling seemed harder work than ever before. Seven or eight overs at a stretch was as much as he could get through before his arm got lower and he began to drop short of a length. Yet he had to keep going, and sometimes came in for merciless punishment. Even when fresh his penetrative powers seemed less, there was no real venom behind his attack. His figures, when cricket finished for the year, were 37 wickets for nearly 32 runs apiece, and it was not much consolation that his batting average, under the easy conditions, rose to 22.

For the County the season was a wretchedly poor one. Shelly, after a bad start, ran into form in August, and he, Lumley, and Arthur Meadows were the most successful batsmen. Revill was still in the Army, and determined to stay in as long as he could; he was flush with his captain's pay, and living an easy, careless life. He got a fortnight's leave in August, and played in three County matches as an amateur, batting as brilliantly as ever. The bowling of the side was the real trouble. Gerald Stokes could not play. Moore and Pearson-Phillips were lost, Lumley proved quite innocuous, and in the early part of the season there was no one capable of taking wickets, other than by accident, except George Lemon and Joe Plant. The former worked as hard as ever, but he was getting a little old for a fast bowler. Plant, older still, had some good days and some bad ones. Between them, however, they had to carry the attack on their shoulders before Teddy's return in June; and Teddy's inability to get back his form and relieve them of some of the burden was the occasion of much disappointment.

There was perhaps another reason for Teddy's comparative failure besides stiffness and poor health. One afternoon towards the end of August Dr. Littlehampton, now President of the Club, asked him:

"Have you had a medical board since your discharge?"

"No, doc."

"I'd be glad to run you over—as a friend, of course."

He made an appointment, and when Teddy presented himself at the surgery conducted a very thorough examination. At the end he said:

"There's nothing organically wrong with you. You should get the malaria right out of your system in six months, if you do what I tell you."

He hesitated for a moment, then went on:

"You're drinking rather a lot, aren't you?"

"I wouldn't say a lot, doc."

"Well, we won't argue about the quantity. The point is nothing could be worse for you. I know the temptation, feeling the way you do at present; it seems to put you on good terms with yourself. But you're not the type that can afford to take a lot of alcohol; you haven't the constitution for it."

He helped Teddy into his jacket.

"I'm not telling you this just out of officiousness, Ted. I think this a rather critical moment for you, in your career, I mean. We both know Lemon and Plant can't last much longer. You're the only man in sight at present who's going to do our bowling for the next fifteen years. There is no reason why you shouldn't work up to the same position as your father, if only you live carefully and keep yourself fit. But you haven't got the physique of George Lemon. You can't expect to drink hard and come up fresh the next morning, not for more than a few years, anyway. And I hate to see good material wasted. It's not only you I'm thinking of, it's the County."

It was perfectly true, of course. During his years of war service he had, by imperceptible degrees, got more and more into the habit of dulling the edge of his misery by drinking. It made his evenings tolerable and worth looking forward to, it gave him sound sleep, and, after a few bad waking minutes, he seldom felt the worse for it next morning. The habit had continued into peace-time, and he could afford to indulge it. He was still getting his forty pounds a year from Grainger and Soulby's, and he had received a substantial war gratuity. What drove him to alcohol was not only its power to revive him when tired and ill, but the fact that he suffered acutely from loneliness. Perhaps he only felt the full impact of Cecil's death now he had returned to the place and the life with which their friendship had been associated. Jim Revill was away, perhaps would not care to renew their old association when he did return; the other cricketers were mostly married, and those of his own age had their own pre-occupations—Shelly his music, Lumley, through bitter disillusion over the war, Socialist politics. Teddy was unhappy for the lack of a background. His boarding house had ceased to exist, and he was living with a retired tradesman and his wife, a respectable elderly couple who could not offer him lively companionship. His small acquaintanceships were mostly made at bars, and not pursued outside them. He never seemed to meet any girls at all.

When he got back from the doctor's, he looked at himself in the mirror. There was no doubt about it, he had lost the freshness of his youth. It was not quite that he was becoming gross; in a way he was better looking than half a dozen years back, because the outlines of his face were firmer. But his fair hair had darkened to a mouse colour, his complexion was sallow, his expression suggestive of discontent. He had once promised to be tall, but had stopped growing at the age of fourteen, and though he had filled out since that time he was slight enough to be in danger of description by that most unpleasant of expressions, a little man.

He was more impressed by the doctor's words than he cared to admit himself. But that night he made a resolution. He would go to Burrington, work on Cousin Phil's farm as a labourer, cut out drinking and get back his health. It was health he needed, to give him back the zest for life, the ambition which, for the time, had forsaken him.

XXII

THE PROGRAMME was carried out. Cousin Phil was bedridden now, and Mrs. Phil dead, but the son, who had returned from London and taken over the farm, made Teddy welcome enough as soon as he understood he was not being asked to produce something for nothing. Plentiful country food, hard exercise in the open air and abstention from all liquor except a pint of beer with his supper, worked wonders for Teddy. He returned to Midhampton in the spring full of strength and confidence;

and a period of success and comparative happiness commenced.

During the following three years, indeed, he made no spectacular advance, but he established himself as the best bowler in the county. Over the whole period he took nearly 400 wickets at a cost of 21 each. Steadiness, nip from the pitch, slight variations of pace, off break, and the ability to swing the new ball, were the qualities on which he chiefly relied, and they exacted general respect. His average would probably have been better if he had not been called on to do so much work. Unfortunately he got very little support. George Lemon's leg injury recurred in 1920, and he disappeared from the game, to return two years later, as hearty, genial, and beery as ever, in an umpire's white coat. Norris, who succeeded him, had neither his pace nor his accuracy. Joe Plant was still at work, and now and then ran through the tail end of the side, but he could no longer bowl for long spells. A young left-hander, Levison, was sometimes effective on sticky wickets. Shelly developed an unexpected if capricious talent for leg-breaks, and Charles Robertson, a schoolmaster, came to the rescue with his energetic fastish stuff in August. But there were days, particularly when Teddy had been over-bowled, when the mediocrity of the attack was cruelly exposed.

It was quite otherwise with the batting, which became almost formidable. It received a very important addition to its strength in 1921, when Nigel Le Mesurier, the brilliant Cambridge University batsman, agreed to play for the County for which he had a residential qualification. Le Mesurier's Cambridge record was so remarkable that his debut was looked forward to with special interest, especially as Midhampton had played no match against his University. He proved to be a cheery Blue with a rather loud and high-pitched voice; his manner towards the professionals was not free from patronage. Lumley and Plant resented being called Jack and Joe, like butlers or grooms, almost at the first meeting. There was, however, no doubt about Le Mesurier's cricket. A glorious 87 in his first innings underlined the importance of the acquisition.

Other recruits of the period were an Oxonian, George Vernon, a stylist given to those wristy off-side shots that were going out of fashion, and Heath, the new wicket-keeper, an awkward-looking left-handed bat who gave a valuable solidity to the team at Number Six or Seven.

Jim Revill was back in 1920—a professional again, but not bearing himself at all like the older type of professional. An officer and gentleman, he expected to be treated as such. He consorted with the amateurs, not exclusively and without arrogance, but with an easy assumption of equality which no one cared to challenge. For he was becoming a great man, a class which seldom get snubbed. He picked up his batting exactly where he had left it; his judgment, daring, and that quickness of eye and foot which enabled him to play his strokes a fraction of a second later than the rest were quite unimpaired by disuse. The prophecy that he would become an England player was quickly realised, and although he only rarely did all that was expected of him in Test Match cricket—his extreme confidence and instinct for showmanship sometimes let him down—there was never any doubt about his place. He became one of the major personalities of the game. "Another Revill Century" was an announcement frequently seen on the posters of the evening papers, whose cartoonists caricatured him freely.

He was not a snob. Just as he paid no particular deference to amateurs, so it never occurred to him to assume any superiority over his professional colleagues. He was sure of himself. He resumed his friendship with Teddy as if it had never been interrupted, but he lifted it now to a place of greater sophistication. The days of sea-side pick-ups were gone; he was generally bored with women, who seemed to pursue him ceaselessly. When he did have dealings with them, he never permitted any ambiguity about his purpose to arise. Unless there was a bedroom round the corner flirtatious dalliance, all the by-play of sex, seldom amused him; he regarded it as a waste of time. As ever, he dressed immaculately, and seemed to have money to burn; he was liberal with drinks and tips, and usually contrived to pay when he went with friends to a place of entertainment. Sometimes he skated on the thin ice of ostentation, but his manners were so good, his charm so genuine, that it was hard for anyone to take offence.

"But where does all the dough come from?" asked Teddy rather bluntly one evening. They had been playing at Lords, and Jim had taken him to dinner at an expensive hotel in Piccadilly. There had been nothing small-minded about his treatment of the menu, and the question was prompted by the order of a famous old brandy, when the meal was over.

Jim grinned, picked up a magazine he had brought in, and turning over the pages, handed it open to Teddy. There was exposed a full-page advertisement, the most prominent feature of which was a photograph of the hero of the day, very radiant and toothy. " 'Mine's Kleenodent', says Jim Revill ", ran the legend underneath.

"You don't suppose I let them do that for love?"

"I shouldn't have thought there was much in it."

"You'd be surprised. There's 'Luster for the hair', too. Horrible stuff; I bought a bottle once, out of curiosity. And what about the 'Jim Revill' bat? A royalty on every one sold. And those articles in the *Gazette*—there's a lot of money in them."

"Do you really write 'em?"

"Not on your life. They let me have the proofs though, and if there's anything too damn silly I cross it out. There's the coaching in April, too—not the usual round, you know, but Dukes and Jews and Rajahs and big pots generally who want to get their boys into the Eton eleven. They pay marvellously—that's what comes of being an 'incomparable stylist', my lad."

He was referring to a phrase used in that morning's *Daily Telegraph.*

"You've got to cash in while you can. I wonder *you* don't look around a bit more, Yule."

Teddy shook his head.

"I'm not big enough," he said. "They may think a bit of me in Midhampton, but that doesn't count. No one outside the county would give a damn what toothpaste I used."

He was not contradicted. Such prizes, it was evident, could only be for the few. Nevertheless, there was a slight but definite change in the general atmosphere of professional cricket these days. It was not only that the players were rather better paid than in 1914; they seemed to belong to a different type. Though Jim Revill was a pre-war player, the full flowering of his personality, in the social background that suited it, would have been impossible before the war.

In those days there had still lingered with the cricket a faint flavour of aristocratic patronage. The days when noblemen had backed the rustics they fancied in single-wicket matches were indeed forgotten. Betting was done with, and Beldhams and Lumpys were no longer loaned to a side to make a match more even. But the later Beldhams and Lumpys enjoyed less independence than their prototypes and were more unequivocally servants; they never expected to be considered as anything else. When a former England captain declared in the late twenties that he prayed God he would never see the day when England was captained by a professional, he was laughed at for his arrogance, but he was only expressing a point of view so universally accepted in his own prime that the question could hardly have arisen. The professionals of whom he was thinking were nearer to the earth, they were generally lovable though sometimes naughty, they had broad provincial accents and a touch of naïveté, they ran to an unseemly but charming corpulence as middle age overtook them. Their world was simpler than that of their successors. They were not exactly snobs, but they knew their place, accepting the values of the gentlemen above them and never questioning their claim to constitute a privileged class. They were not, however, above indulging in racy humour at the expense of those who pressed the claim too ostentatiously; and above all, they had character. You could tell one old pro from another a mile off; each had his own mannerisms, a cock of the cap or a hitching of the waistband, a distinctive bowling action or batting stance.

The new young men entertained no very noticeable reverence for their superiors. They were sensitive and argumentative on the subject of class; matters like the existence of separate dressing-rooms or gates for the two grades, initials or the honorific "Mr." in newspaper scores, the traditional style of the match "Gentlemen v. Players" (they failed to see on whom the joke lay), assumed a new importance to them. They were aware that many amateurs, especially those playing for Counties wealthy enough to take a broad view of their expense account, profited largely from the game without loss of social standing, and they resented it. It was not that their point of view was equalitarian. They did not see themselves as working men demanding their just rights; they tended to look down on manual workers and were more intensely conservative than their predecessors. Instinctively perceiving that their labour was not productive, and might find no place in a socialist economy, they feared and mistrusted socialism. What they sought was not a breakdown of social privilege but an extension of it, to include themselves. So far as it is safe to generalise, they were a true type of petty bourgeois.

Not only had they none of the simplicity of their older brothers, they had none of their distinctiveness. On the field you could hardly tell them apart, and mostly their cricket had the same machine-like uniformity. Off the field, too, they were just like other young men of their class, natty, knowledgeable, their heads full of motor bikes, cars, and presently radios. Their manners were good, good enough to make them quite in the picture at the best hotels. Often it was very hard to tell them from the amateurs. When any confusion of this sort took place, they regarded it as a feather in their caps. They were careful about money, and, very properly, on the make. Most of them had side-lines, small businesses or productive hobbies. There were many more cricketer-footballers than before.

There were, of course, many exceptions, geniuses who were a law to themselves, personalities too strong to be subdued to their environment, lusty plough-boys or proletarians bringing back a breath of the old days. But in general, discretion and a sad monotony were the rule. Some of the joy had gone out of the game and its players.

Teddy was not sure that he liked the new atmosphere so well as the old. Still, these were happy years. He was no longer lonely. The game had brought him a host of acquaintances if few close friends, and the stimulus of an ever-changing scene, the possibilities opened up by the good money he was earning, effectually kept boredom at bay. He was still under the influence of the glamour of the game. It was good to be a cricketer, and he did not want to be anything else. He felt sure he could go on bowling for years, getting better if anything. A benefit would now come as a crown to his career, perhaps fifteen hundred or two thousand pounds, which, safely invested, would look after his old age. But, before that, there would be a dignified dozen years as an umpire, or as a coach to a public school, still in close touch with the game he loved.

Two small shocks came during this period to administer a momentary check to his complacency. One evening in a Midland town he dropped in for a drink at a public house on the way to the hotel. He sat at a table in the Saloon Lounge, and a waiter came listlessly to take his order. There was something familiar about the man's appearance, but it was only when he returned with the drink and bent forward to put it on the table that Teddy recognised him.

"I say!" he said. "Aren't you Bill Brett?"

Bill Brett had been a sturdy utilitarian cricketer who had served the county against which Midhampton was at the moment engaged for several years before the war. Teddy had played against him two or three times.

The waiter looked at him resentfully for a moment. Then his grey, ill face brightened a little.

"It's Ewe Lamb, ain't it?" he said. "Very glad to see you again."

They shook hands, and Teddy offered him a drink. Brett got himself a bitter and sat down; there was no one else in the lounge. Both men were a little constrained.

"I saw you got five of our boys to-day," said Brett. "You're doin' pretty well these days."

"I don't know—pretty hard work. I was surprised you had dropped out—thought you were good for another dozen years."

"Oh, well." Brett shrugged his shoulders. "I got a pint of lead in my chest in '17."

"But didn't you play once or twice, after the war?"

Brett smiled grimly. "That's the trouble. I'd been a sight better off if I hadn't."

"How d'you make that out?"

"It's the pension. My lungs are groggy all right. I'd have got a decent pension if I hadn't returned to my former occupation—that's what they called it. That lets the war out, you can't blame the poor old war if I was fit to go back to work. So I get damn all."

"Rotten luck."

"Of course, I couldn't last. There was a Testimonial Fund. But it didn't come to too much, and it soon went west. This sort of job's all I'm good for. I get tired standing on my feet, and sometimes I get coughing with all the bad air. And the pay's rotten."

"What do you get?"

"Ten a week and a meal. Sometimes I make it up to twenty-five in tips. Still, it keeps me alive. I guess I'll stick it out, the year or two I've got."

There was nothing more to say.

The second incident took place nearer home. Chris Burton, a well-known Midhampton slow bowler of twenty years back, whom no one had seen for many years, cut his throat. At the inquest it was revealed that he had been living in extreme poverty in a town at the other end of the county. He had not applied for relief. He had always been a close, reserved man, and no one had ever known he was in distress. Teddy spoke to Joe Plant, who was very cut up about the matter.

"I can't understand it. He had a benefit. He ought to have been all right."

"Benefit!" Plant made a face. "Don't you take much stock by benefits. If Chris got one hundred and fifty pounds that's all he did."

"Couldn't he get a job?"

"He got rheumaticky. Couldn't run, or stand for long. So he was no good for umpiring and no good for coaching. Last I heard he was keeping chickens. I suppose that went bust, then it was too late for anything else."

As a boy Teddy had seen Burton bowl dozens of times, and he was a little disquieted. It was soon after this that he got the offer of a seasonal job with a Midhampton sports outfitters, to give advice to prospective buyers of cricket gear. There was not much in it, a small commission on all goods sold through him, but he took it on. Minor coaching engagements also came his way in April and he accepted them with more alacrity than before. But he was not seriously disturbed, and the impression soon wore off. Joe Plant must have been exaggerating about benefits. It was well known that a thousand pounds was quite normal—George Hirst had got something like three thousand. Besides, you could insure benefits, there was no need to be afraid of the weather any longer.

He was young, strong, in good health, and in good form. Why should he worry?

XXIII

AT BRIGHTON, one July afternoon in 1922, he and Jim Revill were having tea in the Metropole Winter Garden. It was Friday, and the Sussex match was due to start next day; they had come from Leyton after an early finish. Jim had arranged to spend his nights at Hassocks with some friends, whose car was being sent for him at half past five.

Teddy always liked Brighton. It had a sentimental attraction for him as the scene of his *début* and it had chanced that his later visits to the town had nearly always brought cricket success combined with a lively and stimulating time off the field. He had never been to the famous hotel before. Under ordinary circumstances he would not have dreamed of setting foot inside it, for he had not mentally emancipated himself from the wartime rule that certain resorts were reserved for officers; but Jim had the knack of giving normality to an escapade of this sort. All the same he felt uncomfortable when in the lounge they passed close by Nigel Le Mesurier, who looked at them blankly but made no sign of recognition.

They were a little late, and the Winter Garden was not more than a quarter full. Soon Teddy noticed a very smartly dressed young woman sitting alone at a table a little to his left. She was dark and pretty, with heavily made-up lips and bronze stockings exposed to above the knee by her crossed legs and the short skirts demanded by the period. Her hat was unostentatious, her tailored coat and skirt well-cut but simple, and she had not the air of a courtesan. Every few minutes she raised her brown eyes from the *Sketch* she was reading, and turned them in the direction of Jim Revill.

Teddy moved a knife so as to point in her direction and said: "I believe that girl's trying to get off with you."

Jim nodded. "I know," he said, carelessly.

"She looks rather hot stuff. Why don't you do something about it?"

"What's the use? I'll have to be off in half an hour."

Nevertheless, he turned so as to face the girl more directly, placing his arm gracefully along the back of his chair.

"Not bad," he allowed, after a discreet scrutiny. "Though she's no chicken. She might help you to pass the time away, Yule. What do you say—shall we have her over?"

"What, for me do you mean?"

"Yes, of course."

Teddy deliberated. He was not exactly girl starved these days, but his contacts with the other sex were not romantic. He had been unable to fancy himself in love since his affair with the daughter at the boarding house; there had been no glamour either to his small friendships and flirtations or to his comparatively rare dealings with women of bad character.

"I wouldn't mind," he said. "I expect it'll be the same old story, though—either you or nothing."

Jim laughed. "You wait and see how I crack you up."

He rose, and left the room. On his way back a few minutes later he passed close to the girl's table, and contrived to brush her light bag on to the floor. It was delicately and neatly done; at once they were talking easily, and presently Jim led the girl over to their table. Teddy stood up.

"This is Ted Lamb," said Jim. "Alias Ewe Lamb, or Yule to his friends." He turned to the girl. "You know, I'm awfully sorry—I've a terrible memory for names."

She showed her teeth in a smile. "Desirée Molitor."

"Of course. How could I have forgotten?"

They sat down. "I've a better memory than you, Mr. Revill," said Miss Molitor.

Jim affected surprise. "Why, how did you know me?"

"Well—you're a bit of a celebrity."

Jim kept his promise. In the light talk that followed he saw that Teddy had his fair share, and spoke about his cricket in flattering terms, stretching the truth more than a little.

"You know, Ted's going to be a much bigger man than me—the best bowler since Sydney Barnes."

"Really?" said Miss Molitor.

"I don't believe you've ever heard of Sydney Barnes."

"I can't say I have."

"Well, you can take it from me, in his day he was a much more important person than Jim Revill is now."

"Impossible!" But her intonation was flirtatious and challenging rather than genuinely sarcastic.

She showed very little interest in Teddy, turning her eyes to him each time he spoke for no more than the few seconds required by bare politeness. They had not been talking more than twenty minutes when a maroon-uniformed page-boy came into the Winter Garden, calling out, "Mr. Revill."

"That's me," said Jim, and got up. He explained and apologised to Miss Molitor, who looked a little put out. When Jim had gone she said to Teddy:

"I'm afraid I shall have to be going too."

Teddy took courage. "What's the hurry?" he said. "I was thinking it's time for a drink."

Miss Molitor looked at her wrist watch. "Well, perhaps I might," she answered. "But I shall have to go and dress soon."

She ordered a Manhattan, and Teddy, though he would have preferred whisky or beer, thought proper to do the same. Their conversation, laboured from the beginning, was hardly enlivened when the drinks came. Miss Molitor gave very little help. Too plainly, she was not sufficiently interested to put herself to any trouble. Teddy decided he had made a mistake about her. She had no natural geniality. Her mouth was hard; she was not so pretty as she had seemed at a distance and a great deal older.

The only topic in which she showed any interest was not flattering. She asked him a number of questions about Jim Revill—his character, his habits, his income. "He's frightfully good-looking, isn't he?" she came out with once —her nearest approach to warmth. Teddy answered stiffly. Later, he did manage to elicit a few facts about the lady herself, from questions asked less because he was really interested than because the silences were becoming uncomfortable. She was secretary to a knight, a very important man in the city. He was staying in the hotel now; she had to dine with him at half-past seven (the wrist watch was looked at again) and would probably have to work late into the night. She did not, it appeared, have to work for her living; she did it because she liked it, it kept her in touch with important matters going on behind the scenes in the world of finance.

She refused a second drink. "No, really, I must go," she said, and got up. "I'll be here till Tuesday morning. I'll hope to see you and Mr. Revill again."

It was really not necessary to mention Mr. Revill. Teddy had decided he had no use for Miss Molitor, positively disliked her, in fact, but he felt humiliation. He was fed up with high life. He had sandwiches at a bar in West Street, went to the Hippodrome and got a little drunk.

Next day, however, he was in form. Hove was always his lucky ground, but this time he did better than ever before. Sussex won the toss and stayed at the wickets most of the day for a little over 300, but towards the end Teddy, after bowling with great steadiness and life for three or four hours, suddenly "went mad," taking the last five Sussex wickets in four overs for 7 runs. His figures for the innings were 8 for 73.

The morning after, Sunday, the papers were full of it. Feeling on excellent terms with himself, he decided to go and listen to the band on the West Pier. Jim Revill was with his friends at Hassocks, and it happened that he was alone. He was strolling past the pavilion when he saw Miss Molitor, seated in a deck chair, next to a stoutly built gentleman of late middle age. He raised his hat rather diffidently, but to his surprise was rewarded with a flashing smile—a smile of invitation. He was emboldened to go up to her, was introduced to the elderly gentleman, Sir Maurice Reeves, and took a vacant chair by them.

Sir Maurice proved to be an affable, garrulous party, and he at once took charge of the conversation. He claimed to be an old cricketer, a member of the Zingari team forty years back, and was genially caustic about the modern methods of play. Teddy was in a mood of greater assurance than usual, and courteously disputed some of the buffer's points. They were soon on excellent terms. Miss Molitor now and then put in a question revealing a charming ignorance of the game, and was throughout polite, almost deferential to Teddy. She had read about his bowling feat in the *Express*, and had been "awfully thrilled". She might have been an entirely different person to the chilly minx with whom he contended on Friday. She looked younger and pretty again, too; no doubt on the Friday she had been thoroughly tired out by a week of hard work.

Teddy felt a little puzzled about her relations with the buffer. Were they simply those of employer and secretary, or were they more intimate? Week-ends at Brighton with pretty secretaries were almost a music-hall joke, yet Teddy found it hard to believe that there was anything more between them than a paternal friendship rising out of business. Sir Maurice was surely too old; besides, he did not seem at all possessive. He invited Teddy to lunch at the Metropole, and the three of them had a good meal, with a good Chablis, whisky and liqueur brandy. Sir Maurice got more purple and hearty with each successive course and drink; finally, under the influence of the brandy, Teddy took courage to ask him whether he could spare Miss Molitor from her duties to come to dinner and the show at the Theatre Royal with him on Monday.

Sir Maurice looked rather taken aback for a moment; but his eyes were twinkling as he answered:

"By all means, my boy. All work and no play, eh? I'm sure Desirée will be delighted."

"Of course, sir," Teddy added, rather late. "I'd be very honoured if you would come too."

"No, no, my boy. Not my style of thing. Bed and hot water at half-past nine, that's all I'm good for. You young people go out and enjoy yourselves."

He exchanged with Miss Molitor a swift look of understanding, which Teddy did not observe. Miss Molitor said:

"I think it's very sweet of you, Mr. Lamb. I'll love to come."

Not a word about Jim Revill!

Teddy began to feel a little larger than life size. He judged, however, that it would be tactful to take his leave quickly—from his own point of view, too, he could hardly leave at a more satisfactory point. He went back to his hotel to sleep off his lunch, awaking at five with a bad taste in his mouth, but hardly any diminution of high spirits.

The dinner and theatre party duly came off. Miss Molitor was looking radiant, painfully desirable. Teddy's idea was to be dashing and rather gallant, to carry the thing through on a high plane of sophistication. To help him, he had a drink or two before he called at the Metropole, slightly self-conscious in his rarely used dinner jacket. Unfortunately it worked the wrong way. Instead of quickening and liberating his mind the alcohol slowed down his reactions, and the witty, brilliant things he had planned to say never struggled through to utterance. It was true there were no silences this time. Miss Molitor saw to that; in fact, the interest she displayed in him, his history, his prospects, the economics of his occupation, was quite flattering, if it did at moments rather take on the nature of a cross-examination. Teddy coloured his answers with a certain optimism, and, in his anxiety not to belittle his status, depicted the career of a professional cricketer as one capable of bringing a small fortune to those really suited to it. To advance the same impression he rather spread himself over the menu, suggesting the most expensive dishes. One important thing about the way to handle women he had learned from Jim Revill; if you meant to spend money on them it should be done freely, and not as if it hurt. It was wrong to ask your companion if she would care for a box of chocolates; give it to her. It was wrong to ask what wine she would like, with a hopeful eye on the Graves or Médoc; order something pretty good, unobtrusively, off your own bat. Apart from other considerations you would get credit for a knowledge of the good things of the world.

Teddy carried out the principle, and could see that it was appreciated. At the close of the meal, over coffee and liqueurs, he discreetly sought a little greater detail about his guest's life, and particularly her relations with her employer. But Miss Molitor proved much less ready to answer questions than ask them. In reply to a hint that perhaps the old gentleman was in love with her she told Teddy not to be silly. Sir Maurice was like a kind uncle to her. "He's very generous," she admitted. Teddy could see that generosity, in its more material sense, was a quality on which Miss Molitor placed a high value, and although the theatre was only a few yards away from the restaurant where they had been dining, he decided to order a taxi.

The play was dull, a complicated domestic tangle offering nothing to laugh at and nothing to get thrilled over. For discussions in the intervals they had to fall back on a somewhat superficial appraisal of the acting. "*She's* frightfully good though, isn't she?" Miss Molitor would say, and Teddy, agreeing, would give it out that he didn't think much of *him*. He taxied her back to the Metropole. This had been premeditated, and he had intended some amorous gesture to round off the evening. But when it came to the point he felt tired and utterly incapable of gallantry; he didn't know how to begin. Suppressing the idea that he would be thought backward and unenterprising, he decided that it would be much better mannered, much more truly gentlemanly, not to attempt any such vulgarity as cuddling in a taxi the first time he took the girl out; it smacked too much of demanding a return for the money he had spent on her.

But as the taxi drew up in front of the Metropole she put her hand on his arm.

"Don't get out," she said. "Thanks ever so much, Teddy, and *au revoir*."

Without warning she leaned across and kissed him lightly on the cheek. Then she was gone.

He was drunk with her perfume. He paid off the cab and walked back to his hotel, in a ridiculous ecstasy.

XXIV

MIDHAMPTON had a fixture at the Oval late in August. Teddy phoned up Desirée at Sir Maurice's office the morning after he got to town. Yes, she was free, and would be pleased to dine with him that evening. They went to the Café Royal, where Teddy had previously been with Jim Revill. He liked the old-fashioned plush and gilt of the place, with its suggestion of the wickednesses of an earlier age, and he found the company of the film actors, artists, charlatans and plain business men stimulating to conversation. He would have preferred to stay on, but at about a quarter to nine, in duty bound, he asked Desirée if she would care to go to the pictures. She said she would. They saw a film with Barbara La Marr, who was one of Teddy's favourites and who he now liked to think bore a resemblance to Desirée. The film, on top of the wine he had drunk at the Café Royal, put him in an erotic humour. Desirée lived at Highgate, and it would really have been more sensible to take her home by Tube. But he called for a taxi, Desirée making no objection, and this time he took the initiative. There proved to be no difficulty about the matter whatever. She was ardent and expert, skilfully stimulating his desires by her concessions, half maddening him with her withdrawals. He had never been through such an experience before, and when he left her he had to admit he was hopelessly in love with her.

He left her at the gate of a drab house in a drab crescent, and when next evening he went, at her invitation, to dine with her family, he realised at once that she belonged to practically the same class as himself. He was conscious of relief tinged with disappointment, it made her more accessible but less glamorous. Her mother was dead, and though the two sisters seemed jolly ordinary girls, Teddy did not take a great fancy to the father. He was tall, rather sinister-looking by reason of something the matter with his eyes, and he had the over-careful enunciation of a man afraid of not being thought a gentleman. He seemed to be warmly interested in nothing but money and, like his daughter, questioned Teddy closely about the financial background of professional cricket. A married couple came in afterwards, obvious "best friends", who behaved with a touch of condescension. Teddy was introduced to pontoon, and in less than two hours was relieved of eleven and six. He only became aware that he had been playing for money at the end of the game.

He did not get Desirée alone until quite at the end. At the risk of outstaying his welcome he waited until the other guests had gone, and finally contrived a few words with her at the gate of the tiny front garden. He wanted her to go out with him the next evening. The team was travelling to Canterbury, but in anticipation of another evening with Desirée he had got permission from Arthur Meadows to stay in town, going down to Canterbury early on Saturday morning.

But to his dismay she told him she was not free; she had to work. Teddy did not believe this, and as good as said so.

"Don't tell me the old boy makes you work in the evenings. He's not that sort."

Desirée shrugged her shoulders. "I can't help it—he's my employer, after all."

"I believe you're going on the spree—with him or someone else."

She turned on him with a flash of temper.

"I don't see that it's any business of yours. If you will have it, I *am* going out with Maurice. He's been very good to me—why shouldn't I make his life a little brighter?"

Teddy answered gloomily:

"Question is, how much brighter you make it."

"You're being absolutely insulting. If that's the way you're going to talk, I don't care if I never see you again. It won't break my heart."

Teddy grovelled.

"I'm sorry, Desirée. You must see the way it is with me. You're the most wonderful girl I've ever met. I suppose I'm in love with you."

She answered a little more gently, "Well, you've a funny way of showing your love."

It occurred to Teddy that it was a far from funny way—surely jealousy was the first symptom of love. But he did not say so. He tried to get her to give up her engagement, but she was firm, and they again came near to quarrelling before they parted, a little coolly and without making any arrangements for a future meeting.

But next evening at about half-past ten he took up his stand under a lamp-post in Grogan Crescent and waited. He had to see her again. She would doubtless be angry with him. He hardly knew what he would do if Sir Maurice was to appear with her, escorting her home—but it was hardly likely at his time of life.

For hours he waited, standing still and shifting his weight from one leg to the other, or pacing down, sick with exhaustion and the cigarettes he had smoked. At a little before four he gave it up.

Next morning he arrived in Canterbury, sleepless, chilled, and with a splitting headache. Ill-luck had it that Kent won the toss, and stayed at the wicket all day, Woolley leading with a double century. Teddy's bowling had neither length nor spirit; it was hit all over the place.

By the last post in the evening he received a letter, addressed to him c/o the Midhampton Cricket eleven at Canterbury:

Dear Teddy-Boy,

He was very cross with his Desirée the other night, wasn't he? Foolish boy, to mind her going out with her nice old gentleman when she'd promised to.

Perhaps *she* was rather unkind too. Now, Teddy, you said you might be able to come up from Canterbury for the Sunday. If you still want to I'd really love to see you, we could meet at the Hampstead Tube and go for a walk on the Heath. And then Desirée will try to make it up, and if her Teddy isn't satisfied he shall spank her hard.

Let's say two o'clock, unless you send a telegram.

Love (well, a little anyway),

D.

He arrived at Hampstead before his time, and had to wait twenty minutes. She turned up in a good mood, but he treated her with a certain reserve, replying shortly to everything she said.

"Teddy's very stern," she said, as they branched off from White Stone Pond in the direction of Ken Wood.

He plunged into it.

"Desirée, what time did you get home Friday evening?"

She looked at him quickly.

"What does it matter?"

"I want to know."

"I don't know. About half-past eleven—it may have been twelve."

"Not later?"

"Not much, anyway. Why the fuss?—I was out for the evening."

"You were out for the night. I waited outside your house till four."

"Oh!" Her face crimsoned. "So you were spying on me."

"I wasn't spying. I wanted to see you, even for only a few minutes."

They walked on in silence. Presently Desirée said:

"Why do you bother to come back then?"

"'Cause I love you."

"Let's sit down."

They had reached an unoccupied seat in the enclosed part of the wood. Teddy waited for her to speak.

"You know, Teddy," she said at last, "life hasn't been very easy for me. I was married, in the war, and my husband was killed, after we'd spent three days together. And then, I found there'd been something wrong with the marriage, and I didn't get a widow's pension, only a lot of trouble. I had a very bad time—had to stop a baby—and at last I managed to get a job with Maurice. He was very good to me—gave me things I'd never had before. It wasn't as if I was a young girl any longer—how could I help giving him what he wanted?"

Teddy interrupted. "When you were at the Metropole, were you with him that way?"

"Of course."

"Pretty fool I must have looked—asking his leave to take you out."

"No, you didn't, Teddy. He likes you, he's told me so often."

"That's nice of him."

"He's not jealous of you."

"He's no reason to be, not that I can see. Why doesn't he marry you?"

"Well, because he's married already, for one thing."

"Dirty old dog."

"He's nothing of the kind. He's absolutely above-board. He's told me all along all he can do is to give me presents, make my life easier now. He won't be able to leave me anything when he dies, he has children to be provided for. And he's said over and over again that he'd never stand in my way, he's glad to get a little happiness for as long as it lasts."

Teddy fastened on one phrase.

"What does he mean, stand in your way?"

"Well, if I was to meet anyone I liked, who could look after me more permanently."

"Do you mean marry you?"

"It might be that."

"Would you marry me?"

After a long silence Desirée replied:

"It's absurd, Teddy. What could you offer me?"

"I'm not doing so badly."

"I've been used to certain things. You can't blame me if I think of myself. I've had such a hard time, it's no wonder it's made me cynical."

Teddy experienced a feeling of frustration.

"Don't you care for me at all?"

"I do, Teddy. I like you very much. But marriage—that's different. I'd have to feel pretty sure that I was doing a wise thing."

It was detestable. Yet she was being honest with him; he could not deny that.

"Look here. Supposing I was successful. Really well known, and making money like Jim Revill. Would you marry me?"

"Well—I might."

They got no further in the matter. She asked him back home to tea. Her father and sisters would be out. He went, and it became clear that on her own conditions she was accessible. It looked as if she wanted to bind him to her. But his pride revolted; if he could not have her on honourable terms he would not have her at all. He made no response to her invitations, and she in turn became resentful. He returned late to Canterbury, bitter and miserable.

XXV

THE SEASON ended. As during the previous year Teddy had a good, but not a spectacular record. In common with most other medium-paced bowlers of his type he was finding that most wickets in these days gave him absolutely no help. All over the country groundsmen were treating and doping pitches until all the life was taken out of them. A spun ball would come up as if from a carpet, its chances of beating the bat of a player of ordinary defensive skill being very remote. Further, batsmen had developed their second line of defence to a point where it was hardly worth while to bowl an ordinary off-break or in-swinger. Even if the batsman played it at all, it didn't matter if he missed. There were his pads behind to safeguard his wicket; he had "covered up". In consequence, men like Teddy, except in the rare cases where they were handling a new ball, were driven to the adoption of a defeatist style of bowling. Concentrating, over after over, on a length and direction which made attacking strokes unsafe, they waited for the batsmen to get impatient, to take a risk once too often. If the risk was not taken, a deadlock was reached. The method brought the bowler more maidens, but fewer wickets, and infinitely harder work.

The half promise that he might attain his heart's desire if he could achieve a celebrity comparable to that of Jim Revill, with its financial potentialities, stuck in Teddy's mind. It was evident that the way things were going, he had nothing more to hope for than a moderately prosperous career as a good county player. Yet he felt that he had the ability to go further, if he could only master, or rather get round the conditions working against him. He could not hope to become a much better bowler; could he make himself a more effective one? And if so, how was it to be done? He set himself a winter's task of finding a way.

It happened that Jim Revill was opening a winter cricket school in Chelsea, and he invited Teddy to join the two or three other professional bowlers who were helping him with the venture. Teddy seized the opportunity with alacrity. Not only would he be able to be near Desirée, to get her used to him and perhaps even compel her to love him, but he would have a splendid chance of trying out some ideas, one of which might lift him to a higher plane of achievement next season.

He took Jim into his confidence, both about Desirée and

about his ambition. For his treatment of the former problem he received much worldly advice which seemed excellent at the time of utterance, but not feasible—for him at least—when put to the test of action. The latter was the occasion of long and earnest discussions. Teddy's first idea was to specialise in well-pitched up outswingers bowled from round the wicket, with an exclusively off-side field. The ball would be close enough to the wicket to keep the batsman playing, he would indeed be encouraged to attack; but with a swinging ball and a packed off field it was likely that sooner or later he would make a mistake. Jim Revill, however, pointed out the fallacy. From round the wicket it was very difficult to get a leg-before-wicket decision, and absolutely impossible with leg-breaks or outswingers. Even a straight ball from a right-hander, pitched on the leg stump, would pass the off-side of the wicket. It followed that all it was necessary for a defender to do was to get his body in front of any ball that pitched on the leg side and, with due attention to the possibility of a break back, let the rest alone.

Experiments, undertaken by the two men alone in the school of a morning, proved this to be true. But presently between them they evolved another idea. Suppose Teddy was to concentrate, not on outswingers but on inswingers, reinforced or not by his natural off-break. Suppose he was to bowl them not, as was traditional, outside the off stump and coming in to the batsman, but moving away from him to the leg side. The batsman would have to play anything pitched on the wicket, for the ball might go with the arm, or even move the other way. He could not use his pads, for the ball would generally pitch on or near the wicket. He would have to make a stroke. And waiting for the edged ball would be an intimidating ring of fieldsmen, close in on the leg side; waiting for the hook or full leg hit a couple more, judiciously placed in the deep. Would not all but the very best batsmen be paralysed, find those formerly safe pushes and deflections to the leg, in many cases almost their only run-getting resource, becoming suddenly as dangerous as flicking at the rising ball on the off?

For morning after morning, in strict secrecy, Teddy tried out the theory, with Jim batting against him. He worked out the best speed, the right length, all possible variations which would prevent such an attack from becoming stereotyped. In the end he believed he had got hold of something. It was true that Jim, with his exceptional quickness of eye and foot, was often able to get to the pitch of the ball and punish it safely and severely. But he was often beaten too, and though it was not feasible to set a field, he put up what looked like catches close in; and it was possible by an analysis of his errors to work out a first rough sketch of how the inner ring should be disposed. In February Arthur Meadows, at Teddy's request, called at the school while on a visit to London, and was deeply impressed. He took a knock himself, and was all at sea against this new attack. He was, of course, out of practice, but Teddy had opened by bowling him a dozen balls of his usual type, and they had given no special difficulty. Meadows promised to give this new leg theory a proper trial when practice opened in April. It was to be his last season with the club. He was now well over forty—and he was anxious to make it a successful one.

For Teddy, then, the winter was full of hope. He had taken a bed-sitting-room off the Fulham Road, and he found life in London fascinating. He saw Desirée regularly, but would not meet Sir Maurice again. His jealousy was at times painful, particularly during the week-ends when he knew the two were together, but as far as he was able he gave Desirée no sign of it. He was determined to get her, and at the moment he could do no more to forward his case than display coolness and control. He was always at hand when wanted, he never reproached her, and, disregarding Jim's advice, made no physical love to her. His reward was a feeling that she regarded him with enhanced respect, and seemed to grow to depend on giving him her confidence.

XXVI

APRIL came round at last, and he returned to Midhampton. It was a rainy spring, and opportunities for practice were greatly restricted. In addition, the players were asked not to talk about Teddy's idea; nevertheless, the rumour got round the town that Ewe-Lamb had worked out a new sort of bowling that was going to be a sensation.

The first two county matches were played on wet wickets, judged by Arthur Meadows to be unsuitable for the inauguration of the experiment. In mid-May the weather improved, and for the third match, at Bradford, the conditions looked favourable. To release his bombshell against a side like Yorkshire was to risk allowing it to fizzle out before it was given a chance, but Teddy was eager, and Mr. Meadows, not without some misgiving, gave him a free hand.

Yorkshire batted first, and by four o'clock were all out for 196. Teddy had taken 7 for 53, among his victims being Holmes, Sutcliffe, Oldroyd and Rhodes. The inner ring of fieldsmen had taken four catches—and dropped two more—two had been bowled by the ball which unexpectedly went the wrong way, and the last caught at the wicket. Certainly he bowled in wonderful form, never doing the same thing twice consecutively with regard to length, flight, and swerve, and he had the advantage of surprise on his side, but there could be no doubt whatever of the success of the experiment as such. One or two Yorkshire players were disgusted, one declared it was not cricket at all; but another said to him, "You stick to it, Ewe-Lamb, it's just what the game wants to buck it up. It'll put you in the England Eleven if you're not careful."

To emphasise—to the country at large, for no one on the ground could have any doubts about the matter—that no freak of the wicket was to blame, Vernon, Revill, and Shelly made over 150 for the loss of the former, in the two and a quarter hours that remained for play.

Next day the papers were full of it, but with one or two exceptions they did not appear to realise the significance of what was happening, treating the feat as an exceptionally fine piece of bowling of a normal pattern. Midhampton gained a substantial first innings lead. When Yorkshire went in for a second time, Teddy was not quite so immediately successful, Holmes and Oldroyd sparring with him, rather profitlessly as far as runs were concerned, for a long time, but in the end he had five wickets for 80 odd, and the score failed to reach 300. Midhampton got the 140 required to win for the loss of half the side—their first victory over Yorkshire for many years.

It took the following two matches, against Worcester and Northampton, to really bring Teddy fame. In both cases he had ideal conditions, and was opposed to two sides comparatively weak in batting. So long as the shine was on the ball he proved absolutely deadly, and the picture of the three of the four innings in which he bowled was the same—an early collapse followed by a partial recovery. He had 15 wickets in the first match, and 11 in the second. Midhampton won both and, at the end of

May, stood, for the first time in the county's history, at the head of the Championship table. Teddy was third in the England bowling averages, with 51 wickets at a cost of 11.3 each.

He never really looked back. There came bad days, with slow wickets that did not suit him, or when he lost his length, or could not control his swing, or when he was subdued by resolute and skilful batting, or when the short legs could not hold their catches. But in general he was sailing on a full tide of triumph. He had his first hat-trick in June, and early in August joined the small company of bowlers to take 10 wickets in an innings. And against Glamorgan, set the task of getting 50 on a crumbling wicket, he had an analysis of 8 for 8, bringing about an amazing victory for his county.

As the bowling discovery of the year he became a celebrity—there was no question about that at all. The papers called him the "Q-bowler", and sent special correspondents to report the matches in which Midhampton were engaged. The *Daily Mirror* came out with a full front page photograph of his bowling arm, illustrating his grip. Tom Webster drew cartoons depicting him as a genial wolf in lamb's clothing. Interviews, or articles under his name, on "How I do it", or "Why I do it", or "How I thought of it" appeared in dailies and weeklies. The words "Lamb again" occurred and recurred on the evening posters. A rush of applications for coaching descended on him, mostly from players who fancied themselves as exploiters of "Q-bowling" on Saturday afternoons. The climax was reached on his appearance at Lords for his county in July. Newspaper publicity came to its full height; crowds surrounded him on his way to the practice wickets; little knots of gapers recognised and followed him as he walked to St. John's Wood Road Station at the end of a day's play; he was greeted, when he came out to bat, with an applause beyond anything he had received before. He was picked for the Players against the Gentlemen on the same ground a week later; the match was, however, ruined by rain.

Through it all he moved in a happy mist, yet warily. There were plenty who, publicly and privately, disapproved of "Q-bowling", claiming that it was ruining cricket as a spectacle by rendering impossible those off-side strokes that were the glory of the game. A furious letter to *The Times* demanded legislation against it and received some support. Also, there were not wanting buffers to warn Teddy against women, wine, cigarettes, socialism, and infidelity, but more particularly against "swelled head." He was made to feel they were waiting for him, that he had only to strike a bad patch for them to exclaim that here was another player whose head had been turned by success. To disarm his critics he cultivated an external demeanour of modesty that hardly corresponded to the surging pride and elation within. And at the advice of Jim, who was skilled and experienced in exploiting publicity, he tried to develop a few mannerisms in the field. But here he was less successful. He lacked a real flair for the spectacular, and his personality was without real ebullience. He did not give the cartoonists much to work on.

It was after the Northamptonshire match that he received a wire from Desirée: "Congratulations on great success Love." When he came up to town to play against Middlesex she dined with him at the Café Royal the first evening. She asked him questions about "Q-bowling" but did not seem to follow his earnest explanations. She promised, however, to get the next day off to see him play. To her evident surprise he did not suggest taking her to any place of entertainment, nor did he offer anything much in the way of an apology. "Well, Desirée, if you don't mind I'll see you home now," he said, at the unexpectedly early hour of half past nine. "Got to get a good night's rest and be fit for to-morrow."

They met next evening at the main entrance to Lords, after he had changed. It was the first cricket match she had seen, and she was puzzled; "But it's so dull," she said. "Just patting a ball to and fro. Still, I suppose there must be something in it, people make such a fuss about it." It came out presently that she had seen him, followed by a train of boys, returning from the practice wickets; that she had noticed the special round of applause he had been given when he came out from the pavilion at Number Nine to make a very efficient 18; and that the cartoon in the *Evening News*, all the climax of "Q-bowling" publicity, had made a profound impression on her.

They dined with Jim Revill that evening. Jim, always loyal, laid himself out to be charming, but not in such a way as to draw Desirée's attention away from Teddy to his own more glamorous personality. "I told you so," he said to Desirée, recalling their first meeting. "Here's Yule now, about the biggest man in the game, way up above the rest of us." It was not true, of course. Teddy was indeed the man of the moment, but there was no comparison between his meteor-like rise, which might die out as suddenly as it had come, to Revill's own firmly-rooted reputation. But there was enough appearance of truth to give his words conviction.

When the two men left her, Teddy, anxious for the sanction of his more experienced friend, pressed Jim for his opinion of Desirée. "She's a peach," was practically the only sort of answer he got at first, but later, urged to be more specific, Jim added, "Of course, Yule, I don't quite see why you want to marry her." Teddy insisted, almost angrily, "I *do* want to marry her. I know what you mean, and it's quite true, only I'm not going to share her with anyone else." Jim shrugged his shoulders. "You know best what you want," he answered pacifically.

Of course, Jim Revill was cynical about women, Teddy reflected. Certainly, marriage with Desirée would not be a bed of roses. She was not in love with him, he would never be able to feel she was his absolutely. She had expensive tastes which she would expect to have gratified, and the success of a marriage between them was likely to depend on the extent to which she was able to do this. He doubted if she would bother much about his financial position so long as she could get what she wanted. He was not in short taken in by her, he hardly liked her; unfortunately he loved her. To have her, entirely for his own, in all except perhaps spirit, was worth the paying of a high price. And it was a price he believed he would be able to pay. He was already beginning to make the sort of money of which he had hardly dared to dream, and there would be plenty more to come; so he told himself in this high tide of optimism. There would be tours abroad, lucrative coaching at home or in the Dominions of a winter, a possible business to be started, his benefit (perhaps two benefits), all the little money-making sidelines Jim exploited so successfully.

At the close of the Midhampton match he proposed marriage to Desirée for the second time. She did not give him a definite answer. It was clear that she was not quite sure about him; she had enough knowledge of the world to know how easily a swiftly made reputation can crash into ruins. At the same time she was aware that though he was safe enough at the moment, it was possible to delay too long, for his new importance exposed him to attacks from other quarters. Suppose he fell in love with someone else? She compromised by promising a decision at the end of the season. His position should be clearer then, and, busy as he was, there could hardly be much fear from any rivals in the meantime.

Teddy, indeed, entertained no such thoughts. Being without a natural instinct for promiscuity, and without those qualities of personality which made Jim a target for women's advances, he never even considered that particular exploitation of fame. He was in love, a fact which excluded from his mind the possibility of outside adventures. Besides, truly enough, he was busy. The season drew on. The tide of publicity ebbed slightly after his appearance at Lords, but it seemed as if continued success was solidifying his reputation. A moderate July—with wet wickets at the beginning and a strain which kept him out of the game at the end—was followed by a splendid August. Charles Robertson came into the side and it became possible to work him less, while with the strong batting side getting the hard wickets that suited it, the county side recovered the habit of winning matches. It finished fourth, the best position in its history, and there was no question about the man to whom the main credit was due. Teddy's figures were 187 wickets for a little under 16 runs apiece, giving him sixth place in the averages for the whole country.

The crown of his reward came on the last day of the last match of the year—at Newborough, where he had been invited to play for the first time since 1913. He received it under rather curious circumstances. He had just got into conversation with a former cricketer named Bentley, a man who had been on an M.C.C. tour in Australia a few years before, but who seemed to have retired from the game during the last season. Yet he was only thirty-three. It happened that Teddy had never heard any reason for this, and he said to Bentley:

"I was surprised at your dropping out. Are you through for good?"

Bentley answered with a wry smile, "I reckon I am."

"I suppose you have a good job outside."

"Good enough." Bentley shrugged his shoulders. "I'm a coach at——" he mentioned a well-known northern public school. "But there was no choice about it. I'm no good for any more first class cricket."

"You seem fit enough."

"I'm all right—in general. But I just can't bowl any longer. Here I am, my career finished ten years before my time, because I played too well."

"How do you work that out?"

"You can work it out for yourself. I was picked for that Australian tour, and it finished me. You've no idea what it's like, bowling on those wickets to those batsmen. You have to be as strong as a horse. I always thought I was, but it looks like I wasn't strong enough. I never got any rest, and next season this side I was dead tired and clean out of form. It might still have been all right if I'd got proper rest, but the county couldn't or wouldn't afford to give it to me. It was a dry season too, and the trouble with my foot that started in Australia came back on me, bad. It's hopeless now. I can't bowl at any speed, and it's too late to turn into a slow bowler. I was told last September I would not be re-engaged."

"That's pretty tough luck."

"It might be worse. They voted me five hundred instead of a benefit, and I've got this coaching job. But I miss being out there, when I see all of you on the job. You take my advice, Ewe-Lamb, fight shy of tours."

They chatted about other days. But presently a boy came up with a telegram. It was for Teddy. He opened it, and then, with sober exultation, turned to Bentley.

"It's funny after your talk," he said. "I've just been invited to go on the tour to the West Indies."

"Oh, well," answered Bentley. "That's not Australia."

XXVII

TEDDY AND DESIRÉE were married in November. The wedding took place at Midhampton, and Teddy's colleagues helped to make it a rousing affair, indulging in all the boisterous facetiousness considered proper to such an occasion after seeing the bridal couple out of the church under an archway of crossed bats. Bride and bridegroom looked stiff and silly in the *Daily Sketch* photograph next day.

Arthur Meadows gave a cheque for twenty-five pounds, and Sir Maurice Reeves another for fifty pounds. Teddy was in favour of returning this, but was overruled, Desirée compelling him, very much against his will, to write a brief letter of thanks.

She was also successfully insistent on the honeymoon being spent on the Riviera. She had at first taken it for granted that she would accompany Teddy on the West Indies tour, and when she learned that this would not be permitted she was very upset—less, it seemed, because she would have to bear a three or four months' separation from her husband within a few weeks of her wedding than on account of the loss of a wonderful holiday.

They passed three weeks at a pretentious hotel in Monte Carlo. Most of the time they were in the public rooms Teddy was acutely uncomfortable. He could not accustom himself to the hard diagnostic stare of his fellow guests, particularly fellow British. The servants, particularly the waiters, simply wiped the floor with him, and, by using him with contempt modified by rare relentings into kindness, so played upon his natural wish to do the thing handsomely that he found himself ordering the most extravagant wines and expensive out-of-season dishes. Also, he was bothered about dress. Coming in late from a solitary walk on the first day he committed the solecism of appearing in the restaurant in a lounge suit. Desirée was furious, and would hardly speak to him for the rest of the evening. Nor did the trouble end there. His best suit did not bear comparison with the flashy male elegance around him, while his second best was almost impossible. Desirée, hoping for encounters with millionaires and princes, diplomats and counts out of Oppenheim, found to her chagrin that no one paid her much attention, and she blamed Teddy for this. He had no "chic". She insisted, too, on spending long hours in the lounge watching the people, a pastime that palled on Teddy, who was only really happy when he was able to get out and mooch around the town, savouring the warmth of the sun, the blue of the sea and sky, the glitter and colour of the scene, without social obligation.

What, however, bored him more than anything else, indeed, was the series of long nights he was compelled to spend at the Casino. Desirée revealed an immoderate taste for gambling. She won a hundred and fifty francs at roulette the first night, and thereafter was always after him for money to recover her subsequent losses. He had to stay in the rooms, to be ready to take her back to the hotel when she had had enough, and after the novelty had worn off he found the smoke and perfume-laden atmosphere, the hard green tables, the faces round them, expressing rarely the spirit of adventure or the joy of hazard, more often only calculation and greed, wearisome and depressing almost to tears. He had allowed what he thought was an absurdly generous money margin for the holiday, believing that he could not possibly spend more than half of it, but in the end he saw it was going to be a very close thing. On the last night he had to refuse Desirée money for the gambling rooms, and that did not make the end of the trip any more pleasant. There was some shamefaced under-tipping, in some cases evasion of tipping altogether, and he arrived at Victoria Station with the equivalent of less than two pounds in his pocket.

He was, however, only at the beginning of a series of new expenses. Before the wedding they had undertaken to rent a small villa in Midhampton, in Buller Avenue, not far from Teddy's old home. Desirée, of course, had realised that they would have to live in the town. Her misgivings, however, had been confirmed by her first view of it. "It's dreadfully provincial," she had said. The house was picked on after a period of rather miserable hunting, with some detail always wrong to spoil an otherwise excellent proposition. There had remained no time to furnish it, and with Teddy having to be off on his tour within a fortnight of returning from the South of France, the work became a winter's task devolving on Desirée. She was eager enough to prepare a home of her own. She decided that it would be more economical, and better in every respect, for her to stay with her family in Highgate while Teddy was in the West Indies. She knew how to pick up bargains in London, she could buy better furniture more cheaply, persuading tradesmen to keep it in their shops until the time came for the whole lot to be transported to Midhampton, a few weeks before Teddy's return. The question, however, arose as to how the furniture was to be paid for. The last of Teddy's savings, and the whole of Arthur Meadows' cheque, had gone in Monte Carlo, and Sir Maurice's fifty pounds were quite inadequate to the call. Desirée's suggestion of instalment buying Teddy had obstinately turned down; he had heard tales about hire purchase, and the stuff Desirée had in mind was more expensive than they would need.

Eventually he did a foolish thing. He took out Aunt Stella's money from Grainger and Soulby's. The business had been thriving through and after the War, and he had received his ten pounds every quarter without a hitch. But ten pounds a quarter did not seem much in these days, when he was sometimes getting more in a week; while, with over a thousand pounds down, he could feel himself a man of means. So he took out the money, ignoring the manifest disapproval of the aged Mr. Grainger, and opened a joint account with Desirée at the Midhampton branch of one of the big banks. Desirée was to draw on this for the furnishing, and also for her own needs in the winter. He begged her to try and limit herself to two hundred pounds, and she promised to do so. "But I'll have to get a few clothes, Teddy, darling," she added, as an afterthought.

He was no less in love with her than he had been—if anything more so. For although she was extravagant, self-willed, and shrewish when crossed, she was never dull company, and he could take pride in her smartness and the admiration it evoked. He was immensely proud of having won her, and took delight in recalling her apparent inaccessibility that first day at the Metropole. In moments of passion, too, she gave him, with effortless expertness, almost all he had dreamed of, all except perhaps that little touch of personal surrender that might have persuaded him that thus it was for him, and him alone. It was not coldness, for she was as eager as he to make love, only a sense, seldom failing to visit him in retrospect, that it was only by chance he had been her companion; as far as she was concerned it might as well have been another. She was not in love with him. Teddy sometimes had the idea that if he were to go out one evening, and announce on his return that he had been with a woman of the streets, no more than her pride would be hurt.

Still, she did all he could reasonably expect, with unimpeachable efficiency, and he would not complain of any disloyalty. Directly they became engaged, early in September, she had told Sir Maurice, and he had released her at once. Since then she had lunched with him twice—Teddy refusing to go on both occasions—but he had the best of all possible reasons for knowing that she had not seen him any other time, having been almost constantly in her company himself. There were moments when he had his doubts about the coming winter months of his absence, but he loyally stifled them. Sir Maurice's name was not mentioned by either of them, from the day of their wedding to the day on which Teddy sailed.

XXVIII

AFTER FIVE DAYS of bitter suffering, the company of the ss. *Indaba* found its feet. The Azores was passed, the trade-wind blew steadily behind them, and for days the scene was unvaried—a blue sky and a blue and silver sea, with the sun even warmer as they crept southwards. As it got warmer, there would appear occasional schools of joyously rolling porpoises, or flying fish, single or in companies, skimming fifty yards or more over the gentle undulations of the quiet sea, to bring passengers, pointing and shouting, to the deck rail.

They were happy days, if too strenuous for Teddy's taste. After the stir and racket of his marriage he would have been glad to spend most of the time in his deck chair, sleeping and reading, but he was always being called on to do something; inspect the engine room, talk to someone he didn't want to, play deck games, dance.

He had often heard a liner described as a "floating hotel". The term "floating boarding house" was more applicable to the *Indaba*, only, of course, it was a very superior boarding house, of the type where you pay four or five guineas a week, at Cheltenham or Leamington. There was a baronet on board, also a bishop, both emphatically married; and to help them set the right tone at the Captain's table were a few prosperous West Indian planters or merchants, a major of the Indian Army with his wife, the Captain of the touring side, and a well-known English authoress.

There were, however, no separate quarters for the professional cricketers, who not only mingled freely among their betters, but were actually a good deal sought out by them. There may have been a touch of condescension, but it was very doubtful from which side it proceeded. Some of the persons of consequence were almost too humble in their approach to men who, after all, did get their names regularly into the papers. After making friends with a cricketer they were apt to become elated, and once Teddy overheard the major, to whom he had been talking courteously a few hours before, inform the baronet that "some of those pros are as fine gentlemen as you'll find anywhere." Teddy smiled wryly at the equivocal compliment, which he had heard before.

To complete the contentment of a company of this sort, it was necessary for them to have somebody to despise. This was provided by a mixed proletariat of four—a little elderly market gardener from Hemel Hempstead, who was making a tour on behalf of artificial manures, and who could not, it appeared, afford a dress suit; a parchment-faced Dutch Guianese, equally destitute of proper dress, reputed to have buried three wives after having got three children by each; a Barbadian negro lawyer, very quiet and well-dressed, but who should obviously never have been allowed on the ship at all; and a pale inadequate young English bank clerk, who affronted public opinion by singing rather highbrow songs exceptionally well, at the ship's concert. These were pitied rather than disliked. Desirée would have enjoyed the *Indaba*.

The cricketers lived on board without austerity. Teddy, who had expected that some mild form of training discipline would be imposed, was surprised and a little shocked at the way his team-mates sat up late, till the smoking room bar closed and beyond, not only playing bridge or throwing poker dice, but drinking a great deal, often getting quite rowdy. Not in such a way, he felt, would the pros of his boyhood have comported themselves—his own father, Buckley, Joe Tanner. Some of the younger members never crept into their cabins before half-past three or four; there were whispers of goings-on up on the boat deck with the two or three reasonably attractive girl passengers, who were in the happy position of only having to pick and choose. Teddy, just married, felt a little out of the hunt. However, he drank, danced, sang, and shouted the long evenings away with the rest.

There came a day when it was announced " Barbados, five o'clock to-morrow", and Teddy awoke next morning in a cabin that no longer throbbed and quivered. He put on a dressing gown, went up on deck, and surveyed, in the early light, the low outlines of the island at some half mile's distance away. It looked almost disappointingly untropical. He went below, had his tea, bathed, shaved and dressed.

When he went up again the scene had changed—as full of animation as it had been quiet and still before. The

Harbour Master's launch was alongside, and a black policeman, in a sailor's uniform of a sort Teddy had hitherto only seen in pictures of the time of Nelson, stood at the head of the companion ladder. Attenuated negroes, in sweat grey vests and trousers, strained at the sweeps of the huge lighters bearing down on the ship. More negroes stood up in little row boats, the names of which, painted on boards, they held up above their heads, cajoling passengers to hire them for the shore trip; others, almost naked, solicited for coins to be thrown into the water; "Right, sah. Right, sah!" Teddy threw a sixpence, and four figures, either already in the water or diving from boats, plunged converging after it. Soon they came to the surface, the successful diver slipping the coin into his mouth, and calling out again—"Right, sah, right, sah!"

They got ashore a little before nine. Teddy, and a few others eager to stretch their legs, did not go straight to the hotel, but walked through the narrow streets of Bridgetown, along the almost violently picturesque Careenage, with its small forest of sailing vessel masts upthrust against the hard opal sky and turquoise sea. They were very hot in their lounge suits. Hucksters tried to sell them fruit, beggars importuned them, and presently they got into a cab and drove to their hotel, near the sea, a mile or two out of town. There they ate an enormous breakfast, with flying fish, chicken, rice, yams, sweet potatoes, and other unidentifiable vegetables, after which they were glad to rest for a couple of hours.

It was almost the last rest they were to have. On the *Indaba* they had heard something of West Indian hospitality, and they were now to experience the full weight of it. There were drives through the island—revealing a beauty of which the view from the sea had given no indication—formal affairs at Government House, official dinners, bathing parties on white coral beaches framing a clean warm sea that really had colour in it, cocktail parties, dances. They were plied with drink after drink at clubs, hotels and private houses; rum swizzles, rum punches; egg flips after sea bathes; pony whiskies, at the rate of about four an hour, at the Marine Hotel dance. "Here, I've had about twenty," protested Teddy at this last function, to an affable cocksure Barbadian, who had been giving him details about the M.C.C. team under Mr. Somerset many years before, when he found another pony glass in front of him. "Don't mind that, maan," answered the Barbadian. "You've been dancing, you'll sweat it all out before you go to bed." When Teddy staggered upstairs, narrowly escaping disgracing himself, at about three o'clock, he apprehended dimly that he was in for a bad time. But sure enough, he felt little the worse the next morning.

They had three full days before the first match against the Colony, and they got a little practice between parties. Teddy had expected the conditions and the cricket to be somewhat primitive, but he was surprised by both. The ground at Kensington was bigger than that at Midhampton, and at least as well kept, and the quality of the practice bowling, from barefooted negro ground boys, beyond anything he would have believed possible. It looked as if the tour might not be altogether a picnic from the cricket point of view.

This was amply confirmed by the first Colony match. Barbados won the toss and batted first. The visitors had been told a great deal about the famous Barbadian opening pair, Challenor and Tarilton, then at the peak of their form, but they had discounted something for local pride. They now learned their mistake. Challenor, eager and aggressive, with daring unorthodox shots which only his quickness of eye and muscular co-ordination made possible; Tarilton, very patient, with a stroke production that was a model of correctness, stayed at the wickets till nearly half-past four, each eventually making just over a 100. Later, after a few wickets had gone cheaply, Browne hit up a quick and stylish 50 against tired bowlers. At the close of play the Barbados score stood at 301 for 5. It was quite typical of the Barbadians in the pavilion that they seemed disappointed with the total.

For Teddy, it had been an interesting, if rather heart-breaking day. Although his bowling had never been mastered, he had nothing to show for his hard work, and he could not blame it on sea-legs and too many swizzles. He had been bowling as well as the conditions allowed, perhaps losing some fight after two or three hours in the hot sun. The trouble was that when, after an over or two, the new ball lost its shine, he found he could hardly swing it at all, nor would the gleaming turf wicket—there was little enough turf on it—take an off break worth mentioning. The ball came off fast indeed but at a uniform height and pace; so that altogether his leg trap had no terrors for the first-class batsmen he was attacking. It was some consolation that the other bowlers had done little better. There was one run-out, two batsmen fell to fast bowling when the new ball was taken at 200, the others were rather lucky victims of slow leg-spinners.

There had, however, been nothing dull about the play. The spectators made that impossible. Eager, vociferous, following every ball with the keenest interest, the tattered negroes round the ring constituted a crowd ludicrously different from any to be seen on an English county ground. It was not only their extreme vivacity. The main difference was the somewhat surprising one that they knew the game. Unlike the great majority of cricket watchers in England, who pay their money for thrills, and look for a dividend in the shape of sixes, slashing fours, or flying stumps, these onlookers were stern critics of reckless play, and applauded a skilful defensive shot as much as, if not more than, a drive to the boundary off a half-volley. They shouted advice, but the advice was usually good. They made jokes, impertinent jokes, but they were, when comprehensible, both funny and pointed. "They really know what we're doing here," said a fellow-slip to Teddy, between two overs. The speaker came from a southern county with a following which was decorous but uneducated, and this sort of thing was quite out of his experience.

The match ended in a draw, rather in favour of the Colony. Teddy eventually picked up a few wickets, and also played an innings of 61 which pleased him very much. He found the true Barbados' wickets easy to bat on, once he had got the pace of them. He had got used to the heat, which was tempered most of the time by the strong refreshing trade-wind; and he was beginning to enjoy himself thoroughly when the disaster occurred.

There was a second game against the island before the first match against the West Indies—who had not been given official Test-playing status—was due. Barbados again won the toss, and the M.C.C. seemed to have done very well to get them out for a little less than 300. The next day intermittent but severe rain made play impossible, so that another draw appeared certain. Nor did any other result seem likely for the first hour or so when play was resumed. The wicket was now dead slow and quite harmless, the batsmen's only difficulty being that of forcing the ball for runs on a sodden out-field which killed the power of their strokes.

The ball began popping a bit just before lunch, when the M.C.C. score was 80 for 1. No one suspected what was going to happen, although the suggestion was made that spin bowlers might perhaps be able to make hay if the sun shone. It was not, however, the spin bowlers who caused the trouble, on a pitch that, after the interval, became absolutely terrifying. It was "Barbados Special", the worst wicket in the world, and something quite foreign to English experience, with the fast bowlers making the ball fly stump high, shoulder high, head high, sky high, nobody knowing which it was to be. Making runs, except virtually by accident, was almost an impossibility. To all save the most lion-hearted, the defence of one's person became frankly a more important consideration than the defence of one's wicket.

Five men were out before the 100 was reached, all glad enough to get back to the safety of the pavilion. The indications seemed, however, to be that they would have to go out and face the music again, for nearly 60 were still wanted to avoid follow-on.

It seemed to Teddy, coming out to bat in his usual position at Number Nine, that any attempt to play real cricket was inadvisable. He decided to hit at everything; he had seen forties or fifties fluked on wickets equally impossible if less dangerous. Never having been severely hurt playing cricket he was not unduly intimidated. He got off the mark with a soaring four over cover point's head, and in ten minutes he rattled up 20. Luck seemed to be with him. When he failed to connect the ball missed the stumps, and his mishits did not go to hand. The Barbados bowlers, not unnaturally exploiting their advantage in the hope of gaining a victory over the strongest M.C.C. side ever sent out, were bowling short of a length, a circumstance which had hitherto doubled the terrors of the batsman. Teddy, however, got right back on his stumps and swung his bat freely.

Two consecutive fours on the leg side brought up 130—his luck was holding. The next ball looked the same sort of thing. But it came up higher and much quicker; and

Teddy realised in a fraction of a second that he could neither hit it nor get out of its way.

XXIX

EVEN WHEN he was able to understand that he was not in his cabin on the *Indaba*, unaccountably grown large and airy, but in a two-bed ward in a hospital, it was long before he pieced things out. For several days his own memory refused to bring him nearer to his accident than a few days before it, and he was compelled to take details as a matter of faith.

He had, it appeared, been struck on the temple and received a severe concussion, so severe that he had been unconscious for seventy hours, and at one time in danger of death. Nor was that all. In falling his head had come down hard and full on the top of one of the stumps. The testimony of this wound, at the base of the skull, would remain with him all his life, and the daily dressing of it was, in the meantime, an agonising ordeal.

By degrees he came to understand that the tour was finished as far as he was concerned; it was unlikely indeed that he would be fit to play cricket for many months. The rest of the side was in Trinidad by the time he came round fully. He learned that arrangements had been made to buy him a passage home directly he was well enough to travel, and that his expenses were to be defrayed from a sum left for the purpose by the manager of the team. What remained of this sum, it was made clear, constituted all the payment he would get for the tour. It proved little enough in the end, just sufficient to enable him to pay his way on the ship and travel home to Midhampton from Avonmouth.

Early in March he returned to England, only a week or two ahead of his colleagues. Just before sailing he had received a letter from Desirée, who told him she hoped to have the house ready by the time he got back. A wireless to the ship confirmed this.

She met him at Paddington. She was dressed in a very smart tailored costume of light grey, and looked radiant. Teddy felt a little catch in his throat as he saw her. She was as beautiful, and seemingly as inaccessible as when he had first met her. But she was his.

"Poor darling," she said softly as they came together; and then disengaged herself from his embrace.

Everything was ready, she told him in the taxi. The house was furnished from top to bottom, he was going to get a lovely surprise. In the meantime, she had thought there was nothing he would like better than two or three days in London, and she had taken a room at the Regent Palace Hotel.

Teddy demurred. "But I'd much rather go straight home, D. What I want more'n anything else is rest. I was pretty badly hurt, you know."

"I know, darling." Desirée's voice showed a vestige of irritation. "But you're all right now, aren't you? Your last letter was quite cheerful."

"I'm pretty all right. I get pains in the head though. I was really knocked out badly—you feel this."

He took her hand and placed it against the little cavity at the back of his head. She withdrew it in quick distaste.

"How horrid."

He put his arm round her. "Let's go home to-day, Desirée."

"But we can't possibly *to-day*, Teddy. Maurice is taking

us to dinner at the Carlton. He's arranged it specially, we can't let him down."

Teddy noticed, without much inward comment, that she had quietly assumed he was no longer going to be "stupid" over Maurice. He felt unequal to an argument about that. Instead he said:

"But who's looking after the house?"

"Lillah's up there." Lillah was one of Desirée's sisters. "And I've got a splendid maid."

"Lillah! What's she doing up there?"

"She'll be staying with us for a time. Things aren't so easy for her at home. You said you wouldn't mind, didn't you, Teddy?"

It was true that when Desirée had, before he left England, spoken of having her favourite sister to stay, he had answered lightly that it was a great idea. But he had not envisaged anything more than an occasional brief visit, and he did not believe Desirée had hinted at more. He felt he must make a protest.

"I say, D, I don't want to start anything the moment I come back. But we're not going to be rolling in money. The doctor in Barbados told me I couldn't think of playing cricket for another two or three months. That means I only get the ground wage—no match fees and no talent money, of course."

He struggled. "I mean when you talk about London hotels, and having Lillah to stay, and maids."

She turned on him sharply. "But of course we must have a girl. You ought never to have married me, if you're going to turn mean like this."

He did not reply. His head was beginning to hurt him. He may have shown something, in his eyes, or by the colour of his face. Desirée drew his head to her and kissed him.

"I'm a beast, Teddy. I expect I'm too excited. Never

mind, dear, you'll soon be well, and then you'll look at things more cheerfully."

He found himself crying; he was dismayed by his own weakness.

XXX

THE FURNISHING of the house in Buller Avenue certainly seemed, to Teddy's unpractised eye, to have been capitally done. The stuff was, after all, new—a series of very smart and elegant, polished suites. It was true that, after a time, imperfections of workmanship were disclosed; drawers would not shut, doors would not latch, hinges and handles came off, tables and chairs revealed unequal lengths of leg. But few of these symptoms were evident at once, and the appearance was smart and modern.

"I'm afraid it cost a bit more than we bargained for, darling," said Desirée. "Everything's been so dreadfully dear since the War."

Teddy nodded. "I know. You have paid for it all, haven't you, D?"

"Of course."

"I'd like to have a look at the receipts some time. See how we stand."

Desirée's face clouded a little. "I'll hunt them up," she said.

When he returned to the subject next day she told him she hadn't been able to put her hands on them. They must be at Highgate; she would get them when she went to town. She had formed the habit of running up to London about once a week. Every now and then it would be necessary to get something or other for the house; curtains, chair-covers, kitchen utensils. It was impossible, Desirée always said, to get the right thing in Midhampton.

There was no doubt about her attractiveness these days. She looked younger, more serene, and smarter than ever. There seemed no limit to her elegant costumes and dresses; it took Teddy a full month to catch up with them. Everyone admired her appearance, and he was always receiving congratulations, half doggish, but nevertheless sincere, on his good luck. He was half proud, half dismayed.

"It's lovely," he admitted, when she solicited his admiration for an afternoon frock he had not seen before. "I guess it cost a lot of money, didn't it, D?"

"That's just where you're wrong," she answered. "Lillah and I made it ourselves. A girl can dress on practically nothing if she has taste and sense."

Lillah, he knew, could do clever things with a sewing machine. She was a big, hearty girl, who enjoyed larking, innocently if not always modestly, with the young men who came to the house. She appreciated these guests more than her sister did, though it was for Desirée's sake that Teddy had begun asking people to see them. He was trying to provide her with some distraction in a town he knew she found unexciting; but Desirée regarded most of his friends as common, and was faintly chilly with them. "You've had a better education than all that crowd," she once said. "Now you're becoming somebody you ought to look higher up for your friends." She tried strenuously, but without much success, to improve casual contacts with the upper class and professional people of the town.

One day, when Desirée had gone to London, Teddy missed a business letter he had to answer. It was not in the bureau drawer where he thought he had left it, but there was another drawer into which letters and bills were sometimes shoved promiscuously. This drawer, however, had jammed. Applying, in his irritation, rather more force than he intended he burst it open, to discover that it had not been jammed at all, but locked, and that he had broken the flimsy lock. He did not find the letter he had been seeking, but presently there came to light something else—the missing receipted bills for the furniture. As far as he could make out nearly all the articles purchased were covered, and he was agreeably surprised to find that the whole thing had been done far more cheaply than Desirée had led him to believe; in fact, for a sum well within the limits he had suggested.

"I found those bills," he said to Desirée when she got home. He was anxious to please her. "I think you've done splendidly—it wasn't half as much as I expected."

To his surprise Desirée looked distinctly put out.

"There were all sorts of extras, of course," she told him. "Things I paid for without getting a bill at all. How did you come to find them?"

He explained about the broken drawer, and added, "Why did you lock it anyway?"

She answered eagerly, "I don't remember locking it."

A day or two later Teddy was in the bank cashing a cheque, when it occurred to him it was about time he found out how his balance stood. He had not done this before, perhaps through a tendency he had developed since his accident to let things slide; nor had he directly asked Desirée, who was sensitive to hints of extravagance, how much money she had spent.

The cashier handed him a slip over the counter. When he saw the figure his heart gave a jump. With some difficulty he concealed his dismay from the cashier, and hurried home.

"Four hundred and sixty eight pounds, sixteen shillings!" he stormed. "You've spent over six hundred pounds! Where the hell has it gone to?"

He was really furious. Desirée paled; but she was not the sort to be brow-beaten.

"You'd better not shout at me. Either behave yourself like a gentleman or I'll walk straight out of the house. I'm not going to be spoken to in that tone."

He repeated stubbornly, "Where's it all gone to?"

She shrugged her shoulders. "What did you expect? You *have* to spend money when you start running a house. The two hundred pounds you wanted to stick to was absolutely absurd. Ask anybody."

"Why was it absurd? I've seen the bills—the furniture came to a lot less than two hundred."

"The furniture! That's only part of it. You have to allow for hundreds of odd things when you're starting out, and they all mount up."

"I know what it is!" exclaimed Teddy. "It's all those clothes. You and Lillah never made them—not more than a few, anyway. You've spent hundreds of pounds of my money on clothes."

She turned on him viciously. "Well, what if I have? A girl's got to have clothes to keep her end up. You promised to keep me properly—what did you ever marry me for if you want to get out of your part of the bargain after a few months?"

Teddy was sobered. He asked—"Is that really the only reason why you married me, D?"

"Well, I never pretended to be in love with you, did I?"

Later, in the bedroom that night, she relented. He was still brooding; she went to him as he sat glumly on the bed, taking off his shoes, and kissed the top of his head.

"I know I've been a naughty, extravagant girl, Teddy boy," she said. "It was on my conscience, that's why I was so cross when it came out. I'm mad on clothes, that's the truth, and I've never had a chance to let myself go before. Anyway, I have got value—aren't you at all proud of my appearance?"

He did not withdraw from her caresses.

"It's too much though, D," he said. "However much I make, we can't possibly go on at this rate."

"I know, dear. It's only for once. I'll be as good as gold from now on. And I've got something to show you for it, you must admit. Don't you like me in these?"

She was wearing an elaborate pair of cami-knickers of pale pink silk. Teddy was not completely mollified.

She was, however, determined to coax him round, and he had, in fact, no alternative but to accept the situation. Nevertheless, on two things he stood firm. The maid, who with two able-bodied women in the house was beyond argument a luxury, was given notice; and Desirée was in future to receive a quarterly dress allowance and confine herself to it.

XXXI

AS THE SUMMER came, he spent most of his days down at the county ground. It was strange and rather galling to be out of things, to sit restlessly in the pavilion and watch the tide flow past him. In all the years since he had begun to play regularly for the county he had not been out of more than half a dozen matches—apart from 1919—and he missed the intimate contact with the game that had been his summer life for years past.

Arthur Meadows had retired, and he too now occupied a seat in the pavilion. He and Teddy often sat together, a forlorn pair, but drawing some consolation from each other's company. The new captain was Nigel Le Mesurier. "Give him a little time," said Arthur Meadows once. "He'll settle down all right." It was significant that such a remark should have been elicited from so placid and uncritical a person. All indeed was not well in the Midhampton camp. The over-cheery Blue of a year or two back had developed into a hard and watchful authoritarian, with a sense of social barriers so strong as to be almost anachronistic, and ideals based on those of military discipline. He was a fine player, with a profound knowledge of the game and decided opinions on it, but he had neither tact nor tolerance, and was incapable not so much of understanding other points of view as of apprehending the possibility of their existence.

Le Mesurier had not been captain more than a month before he had got most of the professional staff into a state of mutinous discontent which boded ill for the playing success of the side. He started by picking on Joe Plant, who though verging on fifty was still able to tease the batsmen out often enough to make him an indispensable member of the team. Joe was the most good-natured of men, and his waggery, which had once brought him rebukes, was now accepted as a characteristic and lovable element in the Midhampton cricket atmosphere. But to Le Mesurier, who regarded discipline on the field as the first requisite, his garrulity was anathema. "Stop chattering, Joe," he ordered from mid-off in his first match as captain. "Get on with the game." Joe was hardly able to believe his ears, but he was for the time silenced. A match or two later Le Mesurier started interfering with his field. Few captains care to do this without consultation, except perhaps in the case of an untried youngster; and all Joe's professional pride rose in arms. After an unavailing protest he began to play the old soldier, deliberately bowling in such a way as to expose the need of the field he required.

But Le Mesurier was not deceived. He took him off, and sent him—at his age and after he had spent half a lifetime in the slips—to chase balls in the outfield.

Not only Joe, but all his colleagues, were deeply mortified and indignant at this treatment. Nor was it an isolated case. Small breaches of discipline were punished by fines, by relegation in the batting order, even by temporary dropping from the team. The latter, involving as it did the loss of match fees, was a fairly serious matter. Shelly was subjected to this penalty for arriving at the ground twenty minutes late one morning; Levison, after being once warned, was sent in last for two matches for hitting across a Warwickshire bowler's long hop at a critical moment. A climax was reached when one day Jim Revill, padded up and ready to go out to bat, was told by somebody who happened to look at the batting order pinned on the wall that he was down at Number Four. He had always opened for the county, and he could not at first believe it. He sought out Le Mesurier. "That's quite right, Jim," he was told. "I think you'll be more effective at Four." "But I've always opened," protested Jim. "Not when you've played for England," Le Mesurier corrected him. "Anyway, I'm going to try you at Four." Jim was furious. He had a temper, and a certain sense of his own importance. When his turn came to bat he hit at everything, and was caught in the deep for 17 after ten minutes. Le Mesurier's cold eyes rested on him as he returned to the pavilion, but he said nothing. Next day Jim was informed he was being rested for a match.

He appealed to the Committee, and there was a row. Arthur Meadows and Dr. Littlehampton supported him, but they were out-voted. The weight of the power in the Club, social and financial, still rested in the hands of Colonel Thornborough, and he was a strong supporter of Le Mesurier. He believed that the professionals had been getting spoiled and soft, and that the work of a new broom was needed.

"I shall leave the county," Jim told Teddy afterwards. "I told 'em it was either him or me, and now they'll have to take the consequences."

Teddy advised him to hold out a bit; Le Mesurier would probably ease off when he thought he had asserted himself enough. "Why should I ?"asked Jim, rather unanswerably. "I don't have to knuckle under. I've got a residential qualification for Middlesex already. I may have to drop out a year, but I can fill in with a League club, and make a damn sight more money."

He kept his word, and did pretty well what he pleased for the rest of the season. When the end of it came he announced that he did not intend to renew his engagement. Le Mesurier offered his resignation, but discipline prevailed, and the best bat who had ever played for the county was allowed to leave it.

Even in the team, the captain's position was not one of complete isolation. He had a party among the younger players, some of whom realised that he was susceptible to flattery and ready to make favourites of those who played up to him. The playing results did not approach those of the previous years, but they remained pretty good. Le Mesurier himself had a splendid season. His batting was sounder than before without being noticeably less brilliant, and several times he showed he had the courage and nerve to face a crisis. The press wrote of him as possible England captain of the near future.

Teddy began light practice in June, and was soon playing in the Club and Ground matches, taking things fairly easily. He still got his headaches, but felt much stronger as the season advanced. At the end of July he reappeared for the county and, bowling well within himself, did moderately well. He was no longer, however, the sole exponent of Q-bowling. One or two others had taken it up with success—one bowler indeed was getting even better results than Teddy had the season before. The papers were still full of it, but Teddy's name was less often mentioned. Much of the comment was still hostile; the view that leg-theory was spoiling the game was heard on every hand. Le Mesurier among others was known to dislike it. But it seemed to have established itself as an integral part of the current technique of the game. Teddy felt confident that he would be back in his old form by next year, and there was some reason to hope that he might do better than before. For Levison had come on enormously, and a very promising amateur slow bowler, Newcome, was going to be able to play regularly. This meant that almost for the first time in his career Teddy would not be overworked, and going by all precedents, he should be able to get better figures.

He remained rather worried about money that winter. With fewer match fees and a proportionally smaller share of talent money he had made less in hand than in any year before. Meanwhile his balance at the bank continued to shrink. However close a watch he kept on it, each month's statement showed a decline, even before the season ended. The blame could not be put to the door of Desirée, who seemed to be making a serious effort at economy. With the arrival of September, and practically no money to come in for seven months, the situation became worse. He bitterly regretted that he had turned down a tentative offer, made in Barbados in February, to return to the island and give three months coaching to the schools and clubs. The terms had not been very good, and without strong inducement he had been unwilling to spend a second winter away from Desirée. When, however, he learned of the collapse of his bank balance he had got in touch with the West India Committee in the hope that the offer might be renewed; but another player had already been engaged. It was too late to think of other overseas coaching jobs, and indeed it was a difficult time for getting any outside jobs. Jim's winter school had barely paid its way, and was closed down. The only piece of luck that came to Teddy was a fortnight's tuition after Christmas of a peer's son who had just gone to Harrow. The matting wicket in the stables was inadequately lighted and more than two yards short, the pupil was hopeless, and the pay inconsiderable; but it served as a temporary check to the financial landslide.

This became, nevertheless, increasingly alarming. Nearly thirty pounds went one month. There were coals to buy at this time of the year, and more gas for cooking, and more electricity for lighting had to be consumed. Both he and Desirée succumbed in February to a severe form of 'flu, and Dr. Littlehampton's bill, modest as it was likely to be from so old a friend, had to be faced. It was a little earlier than this that Teddy had fallen into another quarrel with Desirée. He had suggested that for the remainder of the winter at least, Lillah should return to her father. He had nothing against the girl, indeed he liked her, but she was a very hearty eater, and butcher's and grocer's bills hardly seemed to bear out Desirée's dictum that it cost no more to keep three people than two.

The ensuing row blew over, Desirée having her way. Her clinching point was that if Lillah left they would have to get a servant again, which would be more expensive still. She, Desirée, could not be expected to do all the housework herself. Anxious as he was not to behave like an exacting husband Teddy could not argue against this, but he retained some private doubts. He recalled how his Aunt Stella, a very much older woman, had without complaint or apparent strain done all the work in a house very little smaller, and containing not only a full grown man but a somewhat untidy little boy. It was not, of course, fair to compare the two women. Desirée had been "used to things", whereas Aunt Stella had the traditions of a class whose women make light of heavy domestic work.

It was a great relief when April returned, with plenty of coaching, his old job at the sporting outfitters, and the prospects of good summer earnings. His balance at the end of March stood at just over two hundred and fifty pounds —that is not much less than a thousand pounds had gone in eighteen months.—But this he swore should be the rock-bottom. By living with the utmost care, and exploiting every opportunity that came his way, there was no reason why he should not get it back to the five hundred mark in a couple of years or less.

He was strong and well again, his headaches having practically disappeared. Better times were coming; he faced the new season with confidence.

XXXII

AFTERWARDS, he wondered how he could have been so dense as not to have seen it coming. It was true he had received no official intimation. Le Mesurier had been absent with a cold during the later stages of the preliminary practice, and small hints dropped by one or two club officials had not seemed to carry much weight. The opening match was at Leicester. The weather was glorious, the wicket fast and true, but of the sort on which Teddy knew he would bowl effectively. He was feeling very fit, and had helped to improve a moderate Mid-hampton score by hitting up a brisk fifty before being bowled by Astill. The visitors took the field at a quarter past five.

Norris, as usual, bowled the first over, and then the ball was thrown to Teddy. The fielders began to move to the familiar positions; four "leg slips", a forward short-leg, mid on, and deep square leg, with only two men on the off side. It had been a tradition under Arthur Meadows for each man to make straight for his usual place whenever a new bowler went on, avoiding any fuss or waste of time, except when a particular batsman or a particular wicket necessitated some modification of the normal arrangement.

The fieldsmen, however, had hardly started changing when Nigel Le Mesurier advanced to the bowler's wicket and clapped his hands.

"Wash out the leg field," he said.

To Teddy's speechless dismay he proceeded, without consultation, to set the orthodox field for a right hand medium paced bowler. Only one short leg remained—"for the in-swinger", Le Mesurier explained to Teddy. "But I don't want you to bowl it too often while the ball's new. Swing it away mostly, somewhere near the off stump, and let the slips take the catches."

He looked round the field complacently, and then added, "How will that suit you?"

Teddy managed to protest.

"But, skipper, conditions are just right for the leg stuff. Why can't I bowl it to-day?"

"Sorry, Ewe-Lamb. We're putting a stopper on that."

He walked away towards mid-off.

Teddy could hardly hold the ball for chagrin. He got his arm over mechanically, but his mind was not on his task. His first over contained three full tosses and a long hop, and yielded thirteen runs.

"I hope you're not going to sulk, Lamb," said Le Mesurier warningly, at the end of the over.

That seemed the last straw. Teddy answered furiously:—

"I'm not sulking, damn you. I'm bloody upset; you're taking away my bread and butter."

Le Mesurier answered sharply. "Well, mind your language, if you want to stay on the field."

When play was over Teddy apologised. He had up to this time got on quite well with Le Mesurier, and it did not seem impossible to placate him.

"It was the shock of it, skipper," he said. "I'm sorry I burst out, but I do wish you'd think it over again. Remember, it was my bowling the leg stuff that got us fourth in the Championship a couple of years ago."

"That's not the point," Le Mesurier replied. "So long as I'm captain, Midhampton is going to play cricket in the right spirit, with no grubbing for positions or averages. This leg theory is spoiling the game. It started here, and it's going to finish here."

"But you won't get the other counties to see it that way, sir. Why should we put ourselves at a disadvantage?"

"That's their lookout. I tell you, Ewe-Lamb, you're arguing purely from the point of view of results. I'm thinking of the game—and I may say the Committee agrees with me."

"I don't see how you can ignore results. It's results that bring the money in. And now it looks as if there will be a drop in receipts, with Jim Revill gone, and me having to bowl up and down stuff."

Le Mesurier stiffened. The remark was not tactful, bearing in mind the conditions of Revill's departure. It was possible to take it as a reproach, even as a threat; that was how the captain took it.

"That's quite enough, Lamb. We're all the better for the loss of players who aren't men enough to obey orders loyally and cheerfully. There'll be plenty to take their places. England hasn't gone Bolshevik yet, thank God."

Teddy made another attempt later, from a more personal angle. The personal aspect was, of course, of most consequence to him. It was "Q-bowling", devised and perfected mainly by himself, that had lifted him out of the ranks of good ordinary county bowlers, had almost carried him to the threshold of Test cricket, and opened to him all the profitable side-lines available to players who can keep in the headlines. It was indeed, not perhaps his bread and butter, but certainly his jam and cake. If he was compelled to sink back into the ruck, the source of at least half his income would be cut off. The public was notoriously fickle. Even now other bowlers—mere plagiarists—were cashing in on his invention, the child of his brain. Nobody seemed to be stopping them; apparently the originator was to be the only victim. It was heart-breaking. Almost in tears, Teddy tried to express some of this to Le Mesurier, a few weeks later, when he caught him in what seemed a friendly mood.

But the man was adamant. "I'm sorry, Ewe-Lamb. I know it's a bit hard on you, but we have to think of the game. And it's not so bad as you make out. After all, you're a good bowler, the best we've got. It's your skill that got you the wickets, not a rotten theory. You just show a little adaptability, and you'll be tumbling them out as fast as ever."

Events, however, did not seem to bear out this prophecy. At the end of June, Teddy had got fifty odd wickets, not particularly cheaply—he seemed to be back where he had been three seasons before. Le Mesurier and he settled down into a relation of cold enmity; and this was further embittered by an incident which took place early in July.

Batting against Yorkshire, Le Mesurier, who had reached 99 when Teddy joined him, stepped out and played a ball from Roy Kilner gently towards mid-off. He called for a run, but Teddy, who had not backed up very far and knew he could not make the ground, yelled to him to go back. There was plenty of time for Le Mesurier to do so, but instead he came charging on. By the time Teddy realised there was no stopping him, and had begun to run, fully prepared to sacrifice himself, Emmott Robinson had thrown the far wicket down with a lightning return. The batsmen had not crossed, and Le Mesurier was out. White and furious, he snarled at Teddy as he passed him, "You dirty little cad. You did that on purpose."

Nothing could persuade him that Teddy, who was certainly not more than half to blame, had not been indulging in a piece of vindictive retaliation. The episode added discomfort to a situation that was already unpleasant enough.

A little while after this, Teddy was accosted on entering his house one evening by an odd-looking little man in a bowler hat.

"Ah've been waiting on your doorstep nigh ten minutes," he observed with a comic air of grievance. "Seems laike there's nobody at whoam."

"My wife must be out," Teddy said, looking at his visitor curiously.

"Eigh then, it's not your wife I want to talk business with. Though I won't say but it doan't sometimes pay to see the ladies first."

"Come on in," said Teddy.

He led the way into the living-room. The little man removed his bowler, placed it carefully on his knees, and got straight to business.

"Ah represent Burnhamside in Mersey League. Ah'm empowered to offer you five year contract, one year probationary, starting next season."

Teddy pricked up his ears. He had heard quite a lot about the Lancashire and other north country Leagues, where Saturday afternoon cricket was played much in the spirit of professional football, and with much the same atmosphere of excitement. Every year there was a small but steady drain of county professionals into the ranks of the Leagues. They were frowned on by the M.C.C. and county authorities as destructive of the spirit of the game and an element making for its complete commercialisation. Teddy, however, was naturally not in a mood where this view would have much weight with him.

Before he answered, the Lancashire man, appraising him with a shrewd eye, went on:

"I heer tell they won't let thee bowl Q."

"That's true enough," Teddy replied bitterly. "I started it, and now I'm the only fellow in England not allowed to bowl it."

"Oop at Burnhamside thou canst bowl Q or X or Y or Z, no matter what, so be it gets t'wickets. And there's brass in the Leagues, lad. Happen there's no fancy stuff, but there's good solid brass."

He had with him a contract form, all ready for Teddy's signature, and he went over the clauses, adding a kind of running commentary. The offer was of £350 for a little over four months service each year. Most of the matches were played on Saturdays, but there was coaching and game practice on other evenings, and the professional was expected to supervise the preparation of the wickets and see to the condition of the ground generally. The money rewards by no means stopped with the salary, for talent money was liberal and promptly paid, and collections taken on the ground after specially good performances often realised remarkable sums. Further, special private coaching, or part-time work unconnected with cricket, were possible and fully permitted.

Altogether, it looked an attractive proposition, and in Teddy's present state of frustration, potentially much more lucrative than county cricket. He was, in fact, ripe for it, and but for his natural conservations might easily have signed up on the spot. As it was, he asked for a week before giving a decision, and this was readily granted.

Desirée was rather chilling when the proposition was put to her. Burhamside had for her even fewer attractions than Midhampton, and was much farther from London. "I can't bear Lancashire people," she said. "They're so hearty, and inquisitive. I'd simply hate to be slapped on the back and called 'Lass'." Teddy tried to impress her with the money possibilities, but she remained set against the project. "You can be sure their man was making the best of it," she told him.

Arthur Meadows, consulted the next day, was even more decided. He hated the Leagues. "They wait for the counties to train men, spend a lot on them, and make them into cricketers, and then tempt them away with attractive-looking contracts and a lot of false promises. I'm told that in one way and another the money isn't half as good as it looks, and the cricket and the wickets are rotten—enough to spoil you in a year or two. You stick to the county, Ewe-Lamb; this trouble with Le Mesurier will work itself out some way."

Teddy's professional colleagues were divided. Some of them shared the common county players' prejudices against the Leagues, but none happened to have had first-hand experience of them. One or two advised him to accept, on the ground that if Midhampton lost him on top of Jim Revill, it would surely mean the end of Le Mesurier as captain—the two of them might return when he had been got rid of.

Teddy gave the matter much anxious thought. What

eventually prevailed on him to decline the offer was partly Desirée's unabated hostility, and partly the feeling that acceptance would mean the end of big cricket for him. The immediate rewards might be greater, but what about the future? There would be no more profitable publicity, no further chances of tours or really lucrative coaching, no benefit or Indian summer as a first-class umpire to look forward to. Besides, he was not sure he had the right temperament for the brisk, keenly competitive cricket he would be called on to play. His bowling might do all right, but he would be expected to get plenty of runs in quick time; and, except for rare moods of free hitting, his batting method required leisure and good wickets. He had, in spite of his recent set-back, realised his ambition and established himself as one of his county's leading players. It would be wiser to stick to what he had, and trust to time to smooth out his difficulties.

Nevertheless, after he had sent his letter of rejection, he remained a long time liable to sudden qualms of doubt as to whether he had done the right thing. But he could not foresee the extent to which he was to regret his decision later.

XXXIII

THE SUMMER passed without bringing any change in the situation. Teddy's record was slightly worse than in the year before he started exploiting "Q-bowling". His form had not declined, but the standard of batting was rather higher than it had been in the years immediately following the war, and wickets became every year more hopeless for the bowler. There was no likelihood of his getting much better results by the traditional methods, and unless Le Mesurier gave way or resigned the captaincy, real fame, which had approached so near, now seemed to have receded beyond his reach.

But towards the end of the season it struck him that he might still have a chance. Newcombe had proved a disappointment, showing himself to be temperamentally and physically unfitted for three day cricket over a full season; and Joe Plant was at last to retire. This meant that the county would be without a slow right-hander. Why should he not fill the vacancy? Le Mesurier could hardly stop him from altering his attack to that extent. He had always been able to spin the ball, though he had not often done so in matches. It was the slow bowlers who scored, so long as they were good enough. They did not have their hearts broken and their bodies worn out by hours of plugging away on lifeless pitches. They might get knocked about at times, though less in these days when the art of driving seemed almost moribund, but they did get wickets.

He resolved to give the winter to experiment. The problem of finding an indoor pitch was solved by Dr. Littlehampton, who partially boarded up a large disused greenhouse, knocked down a wall in it, laid a strip of coconut matting, and, with due regard to the glass that remained, batted happily and inexhaustibly evening after evening. Sometimes, of course, he was called away, but there were generally present one or two county or near-county players keen enough to take the opportunity of winter practice.

Teddy's first aim was to perfect the leg-spinner. This came without difficulty, indeed he obtained deceptively big breaks on the matting; but it was long before he could achieve any control over pitch. Persistence did it. Two months' regular practice brought him to a point where he could put the ball within a few inches of where he intended, control break and flight, and alter trajectory, pace, and angle of delivery without upsetting his length or "telegraphing" his intention. He had become, in fact, subject to the severer test of match play, a good leg-break bowler. But he was not yet satisfied. He wanted to be able to command the googly, the ball which looks like a leg-break, but comes instead from the off. Here again he experienced the same difficulty with length control, but the trouble did not end there. For, to be effective, the ball had to be disguised, and this he found required a modification of the action he had evolved with such labour for the purpose of bowling leg-spinners. Eventually he worked out a method of delivery which was not particularly graceful or economical of effort, but which he hoped did prevent the batsman from spotting what he was doing with his hand.

Le Mesurier, now in a rather serious quandary about the county's attack, permitted the change, although grudgingly. Teddy's début in his new medium won none of the spectacular success which had attended his "Q-bowling", but it abundantly justified itself. Good slow bowling will always get its reward, and Teddy, after being hustled once or twice early in the season, developed an immaculate steadiness. The only thing he lacked was "devil". He could never quite achieve the fizz from the pitch which made Freeman and one or two others so destructive. But he bowled as he always had, with his head, studying the batsman, varying his leg-break with the googly and the top spinner skilfully and not too prodigally, and he became something of a terror to weak batsmen. His hundredth wicket came in mid-July, and even Le Mesurier was moved to congratulation. He did not, however, fail to point out the moral. "You see, it's just as I told you," he said. "You're good enough to get the results without freak bowling."

All the same, as Teddy realised, it was not quite the same as in his big year. Then he had been doing something original, something to which many of the best batsmen could not find an answer. Now he was bowling, well and resourcefully indeed, but on familiar lines. There were in the country at least half a dozen of his type as good or better than himself. Leg-breaks mixed with googlies had no longer any publicity value.

Just before the season closed a stroke of luck came his way. A well-known Hampshire bowler, who had a regular coaching agreement in New Zealand, broke his leg in a motor-cycle accident, and Teddy received a cable offering him the job. There was only the one winter's work in it, for the injured player had a long term contract, but Teddy accepted with alacrity. It promised not only good money, but the not unwelcome prospect of a change. Desirée and he were bickering more and more these days. Though he would not yet admit it to himself he was beginning to regret his marriage, while she made no effort to conceal her belief that she had made a mistake. Money had been tight. Her expenditure on clothes, her visits to London, had of necessity been curtailed, and such Midhampton society as was open to her bored her and depressed her.

Rather against his expectations, she did not suggest accompanying him on the trip. He supposed she was looking forward to spending a great part of the winter in London. He was not, however, now afraid of her running wild with his money. After the previous trouble he had terminated the joint account, giving her a separate current account into which was paid monthly the not illiberal allowance agreed on. To this he now transferred a hundred pounds, which he thought would prove more than sufficient for the five months or so of his absence. It was considerably more than he was budgeting to spend on himself in the period, and Desirée did not seem dissatisfied.

His winter turned out a very happy one. He liked the country, the climate, and the people. His work was something more than coaching, for he was called on to play much more active cricket than he had expected, on behalf of the club by which he was engaged. He got plenty of runs and a heap of wickets, mostly with his googly, which against inexperienced batting he found profitable to exploit less sparingly than in England. Long spells of bowling brought him a little trouble with his shoulder towards the end of the period, and, from the point of view of cricket, he was not sorry when the time came to return home.

He got back to England in April. The year was 1926, and he found the country in a state of excitement for which he was not prepared, although wireless bulletins on the ship had been full of the coal subsidy and the activities of the T.U.C. Many people seemed to be in a state not far from panic, and persons who had never before taken any interest in public affairs appeared as frantic and dogmatic politicians. Among these was Desirée. He found her looking very attractive and actually younger; the faint beginning of lines which had lately appeared on her face had quite vanished.

She, more than most, had surrendered to the emotions of the hour, and had developed an almost pathological hatred of the working class. "It's like 1914," she said when finally the General Strike was called. "We've got to smash them or be smashed ourselves. *I* think the Government should order the Air Force to bomb the East End, that would teach them a lesson." She spoke with a passion that astonished Teddy.

Cricket was suspended, and Nigel Le Mesurier, an

executive officer of the Organisation for the Maintenance of Supplies, in the intervals when he was not dashing about at his task of supervising the defence of the town's public utility services, conducted a recruiting campaign in which the voluntary principle was modified by threats.

"It's a war," he announced to a special meeting of the playing staff which he had convened, "and we've got to fight to the end. No use putting on kid gloves with these swine, they don't appreciate it. I expect you fellows to join up in the O.M.S. We need men, and every decent fellow has got to do his bit. We won't forget afterwards, either our friends or our enemies. And, understand, there's no room for neutrals. Neutrals *are* enemies, and we'll remember that, when we've won through." And so on.

Most of the players did "join up". Some, like Norris and Heath, needed no urging, others, like Beal and Levison, rather took the line of least resistance, and perhaps hoped for favours to come. The professionals in general did not regard themselves as having any affinity to the working class. Their social habits removed the possibility of sympathy with them, while the very smallness and precariousness of their economic superiority prevented them from taking a broad view. But there was some resistance, and it was Lumley who voiced it. He had been an active member of the local Labour party ever since the war, and was the prospective candidate for the borough at the next election. He answered Le Mesurier without hesitation. "My advice to you all is to mind your own business and keep out of it. This isn't a civil war, it's a struggle by the working class to keep what it's got. And remember, there's no such thing as a coal strike, it's a coal lock-out. Don't let yourself be hypnotised or propagandised into fighting for the interests of people who talk a lot about patriotism, but don't give a damn about anything but keeping profits high and wages low." And so on. Le

Mesurier took up the challenge "That's the sort of Bolshevik twaddle I'd expect to hear from you, Lumley," he retorted. "However, I think I can bank on the rest of you behaving like sportsmen and Englishmen."

The opposition, however, got a party, consisting of Teddy, who trusted Lumley's judgment, and had an inarticulate feeling that with so much hysteria about one could not go far wrong by keeping a cool head, and Shelly, whose music—he now played in a well-known London symphony orchestra every winter—had brought him in touch with a type of intellectual who never went with the popular stream. Both, besides, were enemies of Le Mesurier. Desirée was furious at Teddy's defection. She felt that every one who did not abuse and work against the strikers lost caste. Besides, there was a somewhat artificial spirit of *camaraderie* abroad among the strike breakers. It was possible to meet, on friendly terms, people of social consequence, people who would not have looked at one before. She herself "joined up", helping to run a canteen for voluntary workers at the electric power station. Boys in plus fours wearing O.M.S. badges made much of her, and she was able to find compensations for Teddy's slackness.

XXXIV

WHEN THE general strike broke down and cricket restarted the atmosphere became unpleasant. Le Mesurier neither forgot nor forgave. He had not quite enough power to drop the recalcitrants from the team, but he lost no opportunity of inflicting pin-pricks and small humiliations.

Results suffered, and this was made worse by a disquieting development in Teddy's bowling. He found himself bowling the googly the whole time; his leg-break seemed to have left him. Practice seemed only to make the matter worse. He just could not get the ball to leave his hand early enough. The consequence was that he came in for a great deal of punishment and lost his penetrative power, for the slow off-spinner is by no means a difficult ball to play, its whole value being lost when it is not bowled unexpectedly. Teddy kept trying, occasionally getting the leg-break by accident, but recovering no control over it. His shoulder began to trouble him again, and at his own request he was rested for a fortnight to give him a chance of recovery.

He came back for the home match against Notts. Levison was out of the side with an injured finger, and Norris had not been bowling for more than ten minutes before he developed a strain. A tremendous burden was thus thrown on Teddy. Over after over he struggled, was completely mastered, but had to keep on bowling.

Late in the afternoon he appealed to Le Mesurier. "I can't go on," he said. "My arm's hurting me, badly."

It was an opportunity for the captain. In palliation it must be conceded that he did not realise that Teddy was anything more than dog-tired, and vexed at the punishment he had been receiving. Other bowlers were equally tired, but the attack had to be kept going.

"Get on with your job," he said. "There's nothing the matter with your arm. I don't want any lead-swinging."

At the end of the day Teddy's shoulder was paining him acutely. It was no better in the morning and before going to the ground he went to Dr. Littlehampton in his surgery. "It's absolutely stiff," he said. "Feels like a dislocation."

The doctor made a thorough examination, putting

Teddy through a number of exercises to help him locate the pain and stiffness.

"There's no doubt it's what's been called googlyitis," he told him. "I've heard of cases, though none have ever come my way. You see, in bringing your hand right over your wrist to bowl the wrong 'un, you impose a terrific strain—" he became too technical for Teddy to follow.

In the upshot he was told he must make no attempt to bowl at all until further notice. Dr. Littlehampton made a telephone appointment with the radiologist at the county hospital, and Teddy went up that evening.

When, a day or two later, he went to see the plates Dr. Littlehampton was looking rather serious.

"There's no two ways about it, Teddy," he said. "It's an awful mess. There's hardly a muscle or tendon in your right shoulder that hasn't been torn or displaced. It's going to be a job straightening it all, and you certainly can't play any more cricket this summer. I'm going to send the plates to a friend of mine in London, a specialist, and I may send you after them."

This was a bitter blow indeed. Unlike most of his fellow professionals he had never joined in the disablement insurance scheme—with Midhampton voluntary—that was open to them. Up to a year ago he had never had an injury of any consequence, and after the accident in Barbados he had still foolishly continued to stand out, believing that the chances were all against lightning striking him twice. Now once more he was to pay the penalty. There was only a month of the season to run, but this mischance was going to cost him nearly forty pounds.

It was just about this time too, that he got on to the matter of the bills.

One day when Desirée was in London he was at home when the afternoon post came. There were two letters; the first a note from Dr. Littlehampton making an appointment for him with the London specialist, who was going to give his shoulder treatment. It was a little awkward. The time was mentioned, and he had promised to take Desirée to a big annual charity dinner and dance at the County Hotel on the same evening. The problem was, how was he to get back in time? Pondering over this, he absent-mindedly opened the other letter. It was an account for cosmetics, from a well-known Regent Street firm. The bill was for nearly six pounds, and it was addressed to Lillah.

He called her down from upstairs.

"This is yours, Lillah," he said. "I'm sorry, I opened it by mistake. But what does it all mean?"

Lillah picked up the bill. She turned red.

"It's some things I had," she answered.

"But I don't understand. You don't use stuff like this?"

She looked defiant. "Why shouldn't I?"

He answered brusquely. "I can think of one reason. You can't afford to."

"Dad will pay it all right."

"Nearly six quid? You're telling me!"

It was evident that she was lying. The truth broke on him.

"Look here, Lillah. This is really for Desirée, isn't it?"

He was persistent, and presently it came out. The account was really Desirée's; she had used her sister's name to minimise the risk of detection. Lillah had received two or three bills, and had passed them on. She could not remember the amounts, and she had no idea of the total sum for which she was nominally in debt. She hadn't even been consulted on the matter, just told to hand over any bills addressed to her. Desirée had explained that she would pay them off by degrees from her allowance, she didn't want Teddy to know because he was close with money.

The row that followed when Desirée came home was sharp, but inconclusive. She admitted what Lillah had told Teddy, and accused him of making a fuss over nothing. She would soon pay things off from her allowance, the total amount was nothing in particular. Rather curiously, the brunt of her anger was directed against Lillah. The sisters often quarrelled, but were usually not long in making it up. This time, however, she was implacable; Lillah had been "disloyal". She went on talking of loyalty and disloyalty till Teddy was sick of the words. A day or two later a quarrel flared up on a trivial issue, and, with the bad blood already about, things hard to forgive were said. Lillah went back to Highgate.

Teddy's suspicions were not completely allayed. Feeling rather mean, he kept a close watch on the post. Every now and then an obvious bill came in for Lillah, and in a few months he was able to size up the seriousness of the situation. It was bad enough. Presuming he had everything in, about a hundred and forty pounds were owing for frocks, stockings, shoes, permanent waves, a fifty guinea fur coat he had been told cost five pounds, toilet appliances of all kinds.

He had kept secret about his observations, until he finally confronted Desirée with the results of them. She took it with an unexpected calm.

"You're being a bit of a fool, aren't you, Teddy?" was the first thing she said. "Haven't I told you they're my responsibility? You need never have known. I wasn't going to ask you for more money."

"Well, how are we going to settle them? Even if you saved a pound a week it would take you three years."

"That's my business."

"It isn't. They'd start putting you into court, and you'd have to come to me. I suppose I've got to pay. Luckily the money is there, just about."

It would mean almost the end of what had been Aunt Stella's money. The blood rushed to his head.

"I tell you though, D. If you run up a single more bill of this sort without my knowledge, I shall give you the thrashing of your life."

"And I shall leave you for good and all."

"It'll suit me all right."

She looked at him curiously. "I tell you for the last time, I'm not asking you to pay those bills."

"Of course I've got to pay them."

She shrugged her shoulders.

"Have it your own way then. But don't you blame me."

There was little cordiality left between them now. For an hour here and there they might recapture glimpses of the rather limited happiness of their early married days, but mostly it was bitterness and resentment on one part, coldness and barely concealed dislike on the other.

Teddy had other grounds for disquiet that winter. The specialist, after working on his shoulder over a period of three months, declared he could do no more. There had been a small improvement, there was no longer any pain, but he could not get his arm over effectively above the level of his shoulder. "Keep up the exercises I've given you," were the specialist's last words. "Apart from that, you'll have to leave it to time now."

It was nearly Christmas. "About how long?" Teddy ventured to ask.

The specialist shook his head. "It's impossible to say. But I mustn't encourage you to be too optimistic."

Teddy went to Dr. Littlehampton. "It's next season I'm worrying about," he said. "He told me it was a matter of time, but he was a bit vague."

Dr. Littlehampton did not answer for a minute or so. He went over to the window and began to play with the blind cord.

"Look here, Ewe-Lamb," he said at last. "Dr. Dakins left it to me; and I think I ought to tell you. He's afraid you won't be able to bowl again."

"Not at all?"

"No."

After a silence, Teddy laughed a little hysterically.

"That's a bit of a knock, isn't it?"

"I won't say it's final, old man. You never know, the body has amazing powers of straightening itself out. But the prognosis isn't very hopeful."

"Could they operate?"

"Nothing to be done in that line." Dr. Littlehampton hesitated.

"I tell you what I've had in mind you *might* try. There's manipulative surgery, what they call the bonesetters. I could give you the name of a man who's got some surprising results, and he wouldn't overcharge you—he's a decent fellow. But you must on no account tell anyone I sent you to him—we're supposed to have nothing to do with them."

He scribbled a name and address.

"You mustn't get too discouraged, even if it comes to the worst. After all, you've been in the game quite a time now—it'll see you through. Even if the county hasn't a job for you, there's umpiring—no doubt you'd get specially early consideration after such a piece of hard luck."

Before he left Teddy exacted from the doctor a promise not to mention to anyone the doubts about his future. In his heart of hearts he could not believe that at the age of thirty-three his career was really ended. He shrank from telling Desirée, to put the fear into words seemed to make it more of a reality. But he spent some bad nights, for a week hardly ever sleeping before the small hours. Then he found that two or three pints of beer after dinner stupefied him into unconsciousness. He took to going out on pub-crawls, giving no account at home of what he was up to. But Desirée made no objection and asked no questions.

His first visits in London to Cakebread, the manipulative surgeon, were encouraging. After treatment the stiffness seemed to go, he was even able to fancy that he could get his arm an inch or two higher. But the effect did not last. Each time there was apparently good response, followed by disappointment. Cakebread worked hard, made it a matter of pride, but after half a dozen visits he had to admit there was no more he could do.

XXXV

TEDDY took counsel again with Dr. Littlehampton.

Against his wish he had now to admit that in all probability he was finished as a bowler. The process of realisation had been so gradual that he had at no time felt the full shock. A vein of stubbornness, which he had shown on more than one occasion before, was now working within him.

"Doc," he said. "What do you think of my batting?"

Dr. Littlehampton laughed; and then he realised that the question was by no means a frivolous one.

"Why, I've always looked on you as a very good batsman, Ewe-Lamb—for a bowler."

"But about my general style—is there anything really wrong with it?"

"On the contrary, I've always thought your method exceptionally sound. Of course, you've hardly ever been asked to get runs."

"That's what I'm wondering about. Do you think, with hard work, I could make myself a good bat?"

"I don't see why not."

"It's what I'm going to try. I know I've never batted higher than 8, and never made a 100, though I've got into the eighties a couple of times; and I did average nearly 23 last season but one. But Mr. Meadows would never encourage me to stay in long, he said I'd too much work to do already without that. I've always felt I could be a good defensive bat, if I was allowed to take my time."

Dr. Littlehampton deliberated.

"I won't say you mightn't do it, Ewe-Lamb. You've got the pluck. What about fielding though—your throwing, I mean?"

"That should be all right. I've spent practically all the last five years in the slips, and haven't needed to throw a distance. If I did get put further out, even in the country, there's that underhand flick. I'm pretty sure I can still manage that."

"It sounds all right. But you know, there's one important person you may find hard to convince."

"You mean Mr. Le Mesurier. But surely, I can count on you and Mr. Meadows to see I get a square deal."

"You can do that all right. You'll need a lot of practice, though."

"I know, doc. I've thought of that."

There were a number of winter schools in London now, and Jim Revill was again associated with one of them. Teddy went to town and consulted his old friend, now at the peak of his career, having completed a very successful season with Middlesex. Jim was encouraging.

"There's never been any reason why you shouldn't get a thousand or fifteen hundred runs a year," he told him. "It's simply this, Yule, you've never used your brains over your batting as you have with your bowling. No fault of yours; you've never needed to. And another thing, you've never had time. I'll tell you something. It's only a little step from getting regular twenties and thirties to getting regular sixties and seventies. It's the sort of idea one has about one's own limit. Batting at nine, it's hardly ever you can think in terms of more than about thirty. If you can go in earlier and revise your ideas, the bigger scores will come."

Teddy came up to town twice a week, and Jim gave him an hour's coaching each time. He quickly pointed out the more obvious weaknesses—a propensity to dip at the too wide half-volley, spinning away; a fatal habit of playing back to over-pitched yorkers; an uncertainty in dealing with length balls on his legs. He brought out new strokes, particularly those lucrative leg-side deflections, which Teddy had never been able to master before. But above all, his watchword was Patience. "Your eye's not quite good enough to take bowling by the throat," he said. "You'll have moods when you go mad, but generally your game is to wear them down. Every time you go in, get it in your head that you're going to stay at least two hours."

Teddy had been re-engaged before the disastrous nature of his shoulder trouble was known. There was, however, some surprise when he turned up for practice in April. There had been much sympathy for him, and talk of a testimonial in lieu of a benefit. Very few people were in the secret of his batting ambitions. He had wanted to have something to show before he did any talking.

Le Mesurier said, "Isn't it true the doctors won't let you bowl, Lamb?"

"It's not exactly that, skipper. I can't get my arm over."

"That's very bad luck. What are your plans?"

"I thought I'd try to carry on."

"How, though? You don't mean as a batsman, do you?"

"I've been working very hard at it during the winter."

"Oh! I shouldn't build too high hopes, though—aren't you rather old to switch over?"

"But—you really have come on enormously, Ewe-Lamb," said Arthur Meadows, who was in the secret, but saw him bat for the first time since his decision at the county nets. "It makes me think, wonder if I didn't overdo things when I used to tell you not to trouble about batting."

"I couldn't have done both at once, sir—you were quite right. But d'you think I've any chance now?"

"Every chance. You may have to wait a bit, of course. But I'll do everything I can to see you get a proper show."

Teddy did have to wait. It was mortifying to be on the staff and left out of the team, carrying him back fifteen or more years, to a time when waiting was accompanied by infinite hopes. Le Mesurier, as expected, was altogether against his inclusion. It took two centuries in club and ground matches to overcome his opposition. Actually, however, the time was not unpropitious. Revill's departure had been followed by the loss of George Vernon, who could now only find time to play a fortnight a year; Shelly, Lumley, and Le Mesurier himself were alone able to get runs regularly. The batting needed solidifying. What with this and the mediocrity of the bowling, match after match was lost, and in June, with Midhampton standing last but one in the Championship table, Teddy was at last included in the eleven.

The match was at Bath against Somerset. He was put in at seven—representing a fair, if not particularly generous assessment of his new batting potentialities. Teddy was horribly nervous when he went out to bat, almost for the first time since his very earliest days. He found, however, a good wicket and an attack wanting in hostility. It may have been that the circumstances of his come-back had occasioned some friendly discussion among the Somerset players—at all events, there seemed a singular want of deadliness about the bowling he received. Wickets went down the other end, but Teddy was never in trouble, and carried his bat for 43.

The match was spoiled by rain, and he did not get a second innings. In the next three games of the season he was unfortunate. A combination of bad wickets and unplayable balls prevented him from getting going. His highest was 21. Successive failures added to his nervousness; and the possibility of a complete collapse of this, his last attempt to secure his future in the game, loomed very near. Nor did the early stages of the next match, in London against Surrey, bring him any better luck. On the first day there was one of those heavy dews that sometimes make the Oval wicket really helpful to fast bowlers before lunch, and the visitors were shot out for less than a hundred. Teddy was bowled second ball.

On the second day, after Surrey had run up a winning score, and got three fairly cheap Midhampton wickets, a brief but violent thunderstorm burst over the ground, putting a stop to the day's play. This happened a little before three, and the players found themselves with half a day on their hands. Teddy decided to go to the pictures, and took the tube to Leicester Square.

The show he had thought of seeing was at the Plaza, in Lower Regent Street. Passing by the entrance to the Criterion Restaurant he became aware that a couple, who had just left the restaurant and were walking a few yards ahead of him in the same direction, looked familiar. They were crossing the Circus before he identified them as Desirée and Sir Maurice Reeves.

There was no reason why there should be anything particular in it. Desirée still went to London fairly often, and he understood that she did sometimes lunch with Sir

Maurice on these occasions. He had long taken it fully for granted that all intimate relations between them had ceased as soon as she became engaged to himself. But something about the bearing of the two prevented him from yielding to his first impulse to catch them up and greet them. Sir Maurice, bearing himself with that exaggerated uprightness so characteristic of elderly gallants who will not give in, was looking almost fatuously possessive. And Desirée—before he had recognised her he had taken her for a tart. A trick of chance had given him a new view of her, or rather revived an old one. Suddenly he was filled with the deepest suspicion.

He dropped back a few yards, and followed them along Jermyn Street, down St. James's Square, into King Street. They entered a door on the right. Reaching it, Teddy thought for a moment he had been making a fool of himself. It was a shop for fishing tackle—Sir Maurice was taking Desirée along to help him do his old gentleman's shopping. He decided to put an end to this foolishness by going in and joining them. He pressed down the handle, and found the door was locked.

Then he understood that they had not gone into the shop at all, but into a door at the side of it, obviously leading to a series of flats. There were three bell-pushes with a name under each, and the name under the top one was that of Sir Maurice.

Teddy walked up and down King Street for the time it took him to smoke two cigarettes. His disturbance was extreme. To confront them, possibly quite innocently engaged, with Desirée typing letters perhaps, or chatting over tea cups, would make him look more of a fool than he cared about. Yet if he went away and waited, even if he later trapped Desirée into a lie, he would have no real certainty that she was doing more than conceal from him the bare fact of having been with Sir Maurice. It would be better to force an issue, at the risk of discomfort and humiliation.

He threw his cigarette away, climbed up two pairs of stairs and rang Sir Maurice's top bell. He had made no provision for the possibility of getting no answer. But in a few seconds the door was opened by a manservant in an alpaca jacket. There was nothing furtive about him.

"I'd like to see Sir Maurice Reeves," said Teddy.

"Sir Maurice is not at home, sir."

Teddy's brain moved quickly.

"That's awkward," he said. "It's pretty urgent. I come from his office; it's important I should get hold of him at once."

"I don't think I got your name, sir," was the servant's answer to this.

"He won't know my name. But I wish you'd tell him Mr. Knight asked me to come, and there's no time to lose."

The name "Knight" had come back to him as that of Sir Maurice's clerk—Desirée had often mentioned him as a man of some trust. The manservant evidently knew of him.

"If you wait a moment, sir. I'll make inquiries."

He disappeared down a corridor. Presently Teddy heard a discreet knock, and after a pause, the sound of a door opening. Presently the man came back and said:

"If you'll wait a few minutes, sir, Sir Maurice will see you."

Teddy was given a chair in the hall. In two minutes Sir Maurice came out. "Oh!" was all he said, when he recognised the visitor.

Teddy was prepared.

"I really came to see Desirée, Sir Maurice," he said without emotion. "I understood she'd be here. Your man seemed to think I came from your office."

"He certainly did." Sir Maurice scratched his chin. "What made you think Desirée was here?"

Teddy looked disappointed.

"Isn't she, then?"

"In point of fact, she isn't."

This was all Teddy needed. "Well, how did she get out? By the window or the fire escape? I saw you both come in twenty minutes ago, and I've been outside ever since. I think this makes everything pretty clear."

"Wait a minute!" Sir Maurice empurpled. "Don't be such an impetuous ass, Lamb. Of course Desirée's here. She's doing a little job for me—only reason I didn't want to tell you was because you're liable to make such an infernal fuss if I see her at all. You forget she and I are very old friends."

"I'm not forgetting that a bit," answered Teddy. "All right, if that's all, let me go to her. I told you I wanted to see her."

"All *right*!" Sir Maurice raised his voice; it was evident he was trying to make himself heard down the corridor. "Only give her a minute, Lamb, if you burst in like this you'll give her the shock of her life. I'll go and tell her you're here."

"I'll go myself," said Teddy.

XXXVI

THE INTERVIEW was brief and bitter. Desirée made no attempt at exculpation. She kept cool throughout. "I gave you a hint," she said, "when you were fussing about those bills, but you wouldn't take it. I'm glad you've found out. I won't have to be a hypocrite any more. It's no good cursing each other, the whole thing's been a flop. I think we'd better cut a loss, hadn't we?"

"Suits me all right," answered Teddy.

Sir Maurice intervened with worldly wisdom, directed towards patching up things. Neither paid much attention to him. The break was negotiated in astonishingly swift time. Desirée would get everything of hers out of the Buller Avenue house within the next few days, before Teddy returned to Midhampton.

Teddy never quite knew how he got through that evening. His fluctuations of mood were incomprehensible to himself. Not unnaturally, he got drunk, and he later recollected having given a long account of his matrimonial misadventures to two separate strangers in two separate bars. He had to talk, and a sound instinct told him it was better to talk to people he did not know. But in the first case he assumed the rather swashbuckling rôle of a man who had stood no nonsense and was rejoiced to be his own master again, while in the second he had reached a maudlin stage, and shed tears. When the pubs closed, he staggered into the hotel in Villiers Street where he was staying. He slept heavily, awoke deadly sick at three o'clock, slept again, and finally came to himself, feeling unnaturally fit, and with an extraordinary sense of a burden lifted from his shoulders, at half past nine.

That afternoon at the Oval, on a wicket that rolled out dead easy, he found himself caring about nothing and supremely confident. Everything went right for him, and in three hours he hit up 127. His maiden century in first-class cricket was made under odd circumstances.

XXXVII

IT TOOK TEDDY the greater part of two years to realise that the contractual and legal obligations assumed on marriage do not expire with its dissolution; that the dissolution may indeed add to them instead of bringing emancipation.

The earlier stages of the separation were deceptively easy. No question of divorce arose; each party just went on as before. Among the parties must be included Sir Maurice who had never reconciled himself even to the partial loss of Desirée; and it seemed as if a golden age had been reached in which it was really possible to put back the clock. To all appearances Teddy was free, and, apart from an occasional heartache, not for the Desirée of the last few years, but for the memory of his own idea of her in the earlier days, he was aware only of deep relief and contentment. The rupture had left him with a hundred odd pounds saved from the wreck, and there seemed to be no longer any cause for anxiety about money. Sir Maurice, in his anxiety to avoid the scandal of a divorce, had made it quite clear that he intended to resume full financial responsibility for Desirée.

Early in the New Year Lady Reeves died. The first

Teddy heard of this was when he received an unexpected visit from Desirée, filling him with apprehension. Some of this must have shown in his face, for Desirée laughed and said:

"Don't look so frightened, Teddy. I haven't come to ask you to take me back."

She was looking more than a shade older, Teddy thought—or perhaps a few months absence had enabled him to get a fresh view of her. But her manner was gay and cheerful—a mood he had rarely seen since the early days of the marriage.

They talked, amicably but not without constraint, for a few minutes. Then Desirée said:

"It's about Maurice I came. Did you hear his wife had died?"

"I didn't," Teddy admitted. "Of course I never knew her."

Desirée smiled. "Well, for that matter, no more did I. But—I'll tell you what it is, Teddy. Maurice wants to marry me, after a decent interval. That is if I'm free."

"You mean you want me to divorce you?"

"Or me you." She shrugged her shoulders. "I knew from the beginning that I wasn't really the right wife for you. I don't think it was entirely my fault—it was just we were what they call incompatible. But you don't bear any malice, do you, Teddy?"

"No, Desirée, of course I don't. I wouldn't stand in your way." He thought for a moment. "But what about the divorce business. How would we work it?"

"There are two ways. Of course, you've got the right to divorce me—we'd arrange for Maurice and me to go away somewhere, and you'd have a detective. Of course, that would mean you'd have a lot of trouble with lawyers and people."

"Well, what's the other way?"

She explained it might be simpler (and certainly more chivalrous) if he allowed her to divorce him. There was no stigma these days with a man, and it would save him all trouble bar that attached to spending a night with a strange lady, the receipt of writs, and the putting in of possibly a couple of appearances in Court. She had the procedure at her finger tips, and made the whole thing seem very easy. No question of alimony would arise, as she would be marrying Maurice directly the decree was made absolute. Without saying so directly, she implied that Maurice would consider himself under an obligation if he were allowed to give his gratitude a tangible form.

Apart from the last suggestion, which he brushed aside rather roughly, Teddy saw nothing wrong with the proposition. A lingering distrust of Desirée caused him to defer a decision, but on thinking it over and talking to a few friends he made up his mind to do what was asked. And so, a week or two later, he spent a queer (but virginal) night with a strange woman in a hotel bedroom in Southend.

After this everything went without a hitch. The decree nisi was granted, six months later the decree absolute. The latter was done on a Tuesday. Arrangements for the marriage had been made for Friday, as it had been anticipated that the case would not come off until later in the week.

On Wednesday afternoon Sir Maurice, after a heavy lunch at his Club, had a seizure in the library. He died almost before anyone realised there was anything wrong with him.

Teddy read about this next morning in the newspaper, under the not unfamiliar caption, "Knight dies in Club". He was shocked, and at once wrote a letter of sympathy to Desirée.

He got no answer to this for about three weeks. The

reply, when it did come, while thanking him for his sympathy, was not very emotional in tone. It contained the curious observation that Desirée's solicitors were getting in touch with the solicitors whom he had, rather against his will, because there seemed no sense to it in an undefended suit, been compelled to employ over the divorce. These men of the law would, Desirée gave it to be understood, straighten out the outstanding business connected with the case.

What outstanding business there could be escaped Teddy, but the meaning became clear soon enough. When he was first made to see it, he went straight to his lawyers, who informed him that at this stage there was nothing to be done about it at all. One-third of his income was attached to Desirée for the rest of her life, or until such time as she should re-marry.

Sir Maurice, like so many old gentlemen who feel that it is tempting providence even to think of death, had never bothered to make a will.

XXXVIII

THESE PROCEEDINGS, as has been said, took the better part of two years. By that time Teddy's come-back in the Midhampton eleven was an established thing. But the rest of his career as a county cricketer need not be dealt with at great length.

His arm never made a proper recovery, and the only bowling he did was with lobs on occasions of no seriousness. His batting, however, proved good enough. At his age it was impossible for him to hope that he would ever develop supreme batting skill. He became just a good county batsman, sound and by no means unattractive in method, but without any glimpse of genius, or any hopes of wider recognition. In a way the removal of the burden of high hopes made for greater content, and a less erratic efficiency. He hit his two or three centuries a year, averaged round about thirty, and gave up worrying about his cricket. There seemed no reason why he should not go on in the same way for a good many years.

His personal and professional anxieties and disasters left their mark on him. At thirty-seven, with greying hair, a face that had become peaky, and a figure that had contracted and rounded slightly at the shoulders, he looked much more than forty—a small man, physically uninteresting, and no longer exhibiting that touch of refinement that had formerly characterised him. To the approach of middle age he did not bring the grace and dignity that had been his father's. He got overlooked. He was not notably popular among the younger generation. Generally he was rather silent, almost appearing surly.

He had, indeed, certain standing worries in the years following the break with Desirée. He was never fully reconciled to Le Mesurier, and felt that he had incurred the captain's lasting enmity. A sentimental approach might have straightened things out, but Teddy was not the man to make it. He was careful to give no cause for offence, to evince no failure in respect, and achieved a sort of armed truce. It was necessary for him to do so, for there was now no one on the Committee whom he could call his friend. Dr. Littlehampton had gone to practise in London, and Arthur Meadows, after nearly dying of double pneumonia, was permanently living in South Africa.

More disquieting was the fact that he was living on a seriously reduced income. Apart from the chief drain, the payments made to Desirée, he earned less in talent money than ever before, and the loss of publicity was registered pretty accurately in the loss of his potential outside earning power. Not being able to bowl, employment in a winter school was no longer open to him, and such coaching as he got now was not very lucrative. His market value as a cricketer-writer he found to be ten shillings for a weekly column, four months in the year, in the *Courier*—and this was reduced to eight and six after two years. He was boarding these days, very cheaply, at a house formerly used for theatrical lodgings, which had lost its trade when the County Theatre was converted into a cinema. Yet at times he found it desperately hard to pay his way. Particularly towards the end of each winter, he was forced to bite deep into his savings—what was left of Aunt Stella's money, and the proceeds of the sale of furniture in the Buller Avenue house.

The narrow margin on which he was working made his life a lonely one. But he had always had a taste for solitude, and, although his spirits were low in tone, he was not unhappy. He derived a melancholy, perhaps a morbid pleasure, from living over good days in the past, turning over his *Wisdens*, generally ending up at the now rather grubby plate of the "Five Cricketers of the Year", among whom he had figured after his hour of success as the pioneer of "Q-bowling". He still read a great deal, rather at random, and the cinema was a favourite drug. Sometimes he would emerge from the pictures on a late winter afternoon, to find a world grown dark during his absence from it; and an unaccountable weight would fall on his spirits. Two or three pints of beer would dull the edge of this nameless apprehension, and ensure his night's sleep. He was not greatly disturbed by the desire of women these days. His vitality seemed too low. It was as if his last effort to come back, the effort that had made him a tolerably good batsman, had exhausted all surplus energies.

There came a year—the fortieth of Teddy's life—which brought some hope of a revival of fortune. He found himself exceptionally fit and in great form from the very beginning of practice in April; and by the close of May he had made over 600 runs, playing with a freedom and dash he had never shown before. The past winter had seen the end of his payments to Desirée, who had married an elderly Australian business man, and had gone to live with him in that comfortably remote continent. This release had taken place at a fortunate time, for this was Teddy's benefit year, and he had entertained some idea that he would be deprived of part of the proceeds to swell the alimony.

The Northamptonshire match in early July had been allotted to him. It was not a bad fixture to have—better perhaps than a game with a more powerful county—for the standard of cricket in Midhampton had declined, with the batting a little and the bowling very much below normal, so that defeat in two days at the hands of a strong side was by no means an uncommon experience.

Teddy was now fairly familiar with the economics of benefit matches, and no longer clung to the inflated notions of making a fortune he had held in the buoyant early days. He knew that the beneficiary had to make himself responsible for the entire expenses of the match-wages, not only of players and umpires, but of almost the entire staff employed on the ground—scorers, score-board operators, gatemen, and so on. The benefit consisted of what was left when these payments had been made, plus what was to be got from a public subscription list, and the proceeds of a limited number of collections allowed to be taken on each ground in the county on which first-class matches were played. It was evident that in the case of a match being spoiled by bad weather, or getting a small attendance for any other reason, the man responsible for the charges would be heavily out of pocket—and indeed as the Midhampton yearly budget almost invariably showed a loss, this amounted to a probability rather than a possibility. To safeguard oneself against this loss it was possible to insure one's benefit, but the premiums were calculated on the takings for the same match over a period of years, and in the case of a poorly supported county were bound to be high. The question was—should one insure or take a chance? Lumley, a few years ago, had had a good benefit turned into a moderate one by paying the severe premium. Shelly had gambled and got away with it. Joe Plant had gambled and done badly. But one could not go by others' experience. It was purely a matter of luck.

After much consultation and thought, Teddy decided that he dared not leave it all to hazard. The small remainder of his savings went to give him a limited cover—he would not borrow money to make himself completely secure. From the moment of committing himself in this limited way, he followed the weather with painful anxiety. He lost form and sleep. He went over figures again and again, trying to put them in a reassuring shape. But at last the Saturday came, a spell of hot weather remaining mercifully unbroken. The attendance was good, distinctly above the average, and Teddy, getting a heart-warming ovation as he came out to bat at what was now his customary position of Number Five, was uplifted to a mood of carefree confidence, hitting up a dashing 77. The day's play closed with Northants having replied with 29 for 1 to Midhampton's first innings total of 312—an entirely satisfactory position, promising a full and interesting three days cricket.

And then—there came a violent thunderstorm on the Sunday. On Monday the weather was perfect again; but the wicket had been irretrievably ruined. A fair crowd saw Northants skittled out twice, for 141 and 82. The bitterest feature of this tragic victory was that Teddy, at second slip, was offered no fewer than five catches, and was unable to drop one. In this cruel fashion, his benefit match was reduced from three days to two.

When, near the end of the season, the last of the collections came in and the subscription list was closed, he was able to see exactly where he stood—just over seventeen pounds better off than he was before paying off the insurance premium. If he had not insured at all, he would have been heavily in debt to the Club.

XXXIX

HE FINISHED the season fairly well, with an average of 36, the highest in his career. But towards the end he found himself getting very tired, and almost anxious to get out as soon as he had made 50 or so. Long days in the field too—and there were many of these for Midhampton in these lean years—took their toll of him. The eternal up and down, in the slips, hour after hour, left him nearly prostrate when the reaction came at the end of the day's play. The end of the last match in August was a blessed release. He had never felt like that before.

Early in the New Year he had an attack of acute lumbago. He made a slow and painful recovery, and was not properly fit when practice started. He failed badly in the first two matches, played in bitterly cold weather. Presently, when the sun came out, he began to loosen up, and did better. But two or three good innings in June were followed by a bad patch, from which he seemed unable to recover. He was not seeing the ball so quickly, and frequently mistimed through hurrying his strokes. Luck went against him; if there was an accident, a run-out or a play-on—or if a particularly unplayable ball was bowled, or a superlative catch was made, he was the victim. His best score in July was 35, made with perversely effortless skill at a moment when runs were of no value whatever.

What was worse, his fielding began to deteriorate. His reactions were slower, his eye and muscles less responsive to the exacting demands made of slip fielders, and he began to put them on the ground once or twice too often. Late in July Le Mesurier moved him to mid-on—an ominous change. He had more time in his new position, and did well enough in getting to balls which went reasonably near him. But of course he was called on to do a certain amount of running, and he had lost his pace.

One day at Leyton he was sent three times in an over to chase forcing shots on the on side. On the last occasion, running towards the boundary, he heard a voice from the crowd—"Pick 'em up, daddy!" followed by a general guffaw. He concealed his mortification, but he was profoundly shocked.

Of course, he was no longer a young man. He had been saying that to himself for quite a few years now, but had never before felt it as being true. Yet he was not really old for a cricketer—not long past forty. He should be good for another half dozen years at least. If only he didn't get so tired. He recalled what Dr. Littlehampton had told him, years ago, that he had not the sort of constitution he could afford to take liberties with. He would submit himself to a severe regime of training during the coming off-season—be careful what he ate, knock off those extra drinks he had been taking of late, in fact give up drink altogether.

Careful living would give him reserves of strength to draw on.

One morning a week later, back in Midhampton, he came down to his breakfast in good spirits. He was feeling better than he had for some time, and the day before he had taken a really good 57 off the Lancashire bowlers. He read a laudatory account of his innings in the *Courier*, and then picked up a letter, which he had previously glanced at and taken for a bill. But the envelope was stamped with the name of the County Club, and his heart suddenly misgave him. He hastily opened the letter.

Dear Lamb,

At a meeting of the Committee held to-day, it was decided that certain players would not be re-engaged next season. I am sorry to say your name is on the list. I hasten to notify you, so that you will have plenty of time to make your arrangements.

The Committee desires me to convey to you their appreciation of your many years of splendid service, and to wish you all success and good luck in the future. May I also add my personal good wishes?

Sincerely yours,

EDWARD T. GAUL (*Secretary*).

He went early to the ground, and found the secretary in his office. He greeted Teddy a little self-consciously.

"You mustn't be upset, Ewe-Lamb," he said. "You've had a good run—been one of the great figures in the county. And you're not finished with the game—some way or another I don't mind betting you'll be in it for twenty or twenty-five years more. But time catches up with us all in the end."

Teddy achieved a forced calm.

"Look here, Mr. Gaul," he said. "I know there's no

sentiment about the business side of county cricket. If you can't keep up you drop out. But I'm not really through. Remember I was ill last winter, and I never really recovered until just lately. I'm all right now; I did all right yesterday, didn't I? Can't you persuade them to give me another year?—then if they feel the same way I won't have any grouse. They won't regret it. I swear they won't."

Mr. Gaul shrugged his shoulders.

"There's nothing I can do," he said. "I'm only the mouth-piece. Of course, if you were to approach the members of the Committee personally you might do something. But it wouldn't be fair of me to give you too much hope."

"But it's such short notice."

"I don't know about that. In lots of counties a professional doesn't hear his agreement's not being renewed till half way through the winter. You've got over eight months to get fixed up for next season—and I haven't the slightest doubt you will."

Teddy went the rounds of the Committee. He found a tendency in each individual to shift the responsibility on to other shoulders. He was given little encouragement to believe that the decision was likely to be reversed, but Gerald Stokes, who seemed more open to argument than the others, promised to raise the subject again if Teddy's form for the remainder of the season seemed to justify it.

His last interview was with Le Mesurier, whom he recognised as the main agent of his dismissal.

"I know we haven't always hit it off, skipper. I'm sure you don't bear me a grudge for old differences. I know you can get me another year to prove I'm not finished. I'd be grateful if you would—more grateful than I can say.

Le Mesurier looked at him steadily.

"I'm sure you're not suggesting I'd let any personal considerations affect my judgment."

Teddy stammered: "No, skipper, of course not."

"That's all right, then. We all have to think of the interests of the County. I'll be frank with you, Lamb. If it was only a question of your batting, we might carry you a few years longer. But the trouble is, you're dead weight in the field. We've got to get younger blood in the side."

"It's only because I've been in poor health. I can get back my fielding. If I go in strict training."

"You must pardon me for thinking you're over-optimistic."

The painful truth was that Teddy was in far better health than at any time since the beginning of the year. In the next few matches things went his way—runs came fairly freely, the catches stuck in his hands. He reminded Gerald Stokes of his promise, and was told the matter would be brought up when the Committee met, on the second day of the last match of the season.

When the day's play was over he was told by Mr. Gaul that the Committee had reviewed his case, but was unable to alter its decision.

At five o'clock on the following afternoon, Teddy came out to bat for the last time for Midhampton. The match was with Sussex—the county against which he had made his début. Thus was the cycle completed. Of the men who had played at Hove, in that match long ago, not one was left in the Sussex side—though Fender still played for Surrey, and Robert Relf for a minor county. Of the Midhampton side, Lumley and Teddy alone remained. Jim Revill was still getting hundreds for Middlesex, and Shelly had only dropped out the year before.

There was no hope of Midhampton winning the game, only of playing out time. The public announcement that Teddy would not be playing next summer had been made, and it was generally known that this was his last match. As he came out to bat—at Number Seven now—someone in the pavilion started a cheer—"Good old Ted"; and it was taken up and accompanied him all the way to the wicket, where Duleepsinhji came up and smiled and patted him on the back. "Good old Ted"—it was a bitter-sweet moment. It had been young Ted, or Ewe-Lamb, not so long ago.

He faced the bowling, calmly resolved to take special care, to finish if he could with a gesture. Quite soon he realised that the Sussex bowlers were making not the slightest effort to get him out. They had been overtaken by that chivalrous camaraderie, amounting almost to sentimentality, which comes over all good cricketers at certain junctures. There was nothing much at stake in this last match of the season; and old Ted was to be given a run for his money. But at the other end there was no relaxation, and at twenty-past six the ninth wicket fell.

Even then Teddy could feel no hostility about the attack. It didn't really matter to Sussex about winning the match, what did matter was that he should get his fifty. And off the last ball of the day, an obliging long hop from James Parks, he got it, with a good clean hook to the pavilion rails. The exigencies of the little drama had been fulfilled—he had "saved the match".

"Well, that's the end of that," he said, as he ran out of the applause and reached the dressing-room. The other players clustered round him, congratulating and making much of him; curiously moved, for it was a moment which must come to them all. Teddy took it quietly, smiling and chaffing back. It was good to have appearances to keep up; it helped him out. He wasn't going to shed tears all over the dressing-room.

XL

FROM THE MOMENT when he first heard his fate it was clear to Teddy that there was only one course open to him. Being thrown on the labour market in early middle age with no qualifications whatever except his skill at and knowledge of cricket, he was restricted even with regard to the very limited number of occupations connected with the game. He could not hope for a contract with a northern League club since he had lost his bowling, and the same disability reduced the likelihood of his getting a permanent coaching job at a school to vanishing point. It had then to be umpiring, and he immediately sent in his application to be considered for next year's list.

He had nearly three months to wait before the meetings of the First and Second class captains who made the selections; and they were anxious months. He had a little over fifty pounds saved, just enough to carry him through the winter if he used the utmost care. But it was not pleasant to think about what was to happen afterwards, if he failed to get work. In anticipation of the worst he left his lodgings and went to board in a very poor quarter of the town, near the Railway Station. The street was, in fact, a slum, airless, insanitary, decaying, loud all day with the yells of children playing or being thrashed. All Teddy's instincts for respectability revolted against such a habitation, but if he was to get through the winter no better alternative presented itself. In the meantime he looked round for work, but rather half-heartedly; so long as his hopes were pinned on umpiring he did not want to show his own town the straits to which he was reduced by accepting too humble a job. In any case he got no encouragement, except a qualified promise that he might be taken on as a supplementary postman in the Christmas rush.

The captains met at the end of November. A day or two later he received a letter—he was appointed to the list of second-class umpires. He had hoped for better. There were one or two retirements among first-class umpires that year, and he believed that if Le Mesurier had spoken a word for him he would have gone straight into the higher class. However, it was something and it was up to him to make the best of it. He got through the winter somehow, making a close study of the Laws of Cricket, the Instructions to Umpires, and a handbook raising knotty problems and giving the answers. He was surprised to find quite a few gaps in his knowledge, but when the time came for him to take up his duties he felt confident of his ability to deal with anything that came up.

There followed two years wherein he had to reconcile himself to a lower living standard than he had ever experienced. Employment was not continuous even throughout the season, the pay was not particularly good, and out of it had to come not only savings for the off season, but travelling and living expenses that were often quite considerable. Yet there were compensations. It was possible to pick up a small fee here and there by umpiring for club matches between the county fixtures. The job, too, took him into corners of England he had never seen before, and he had not quite lost his early pleasurable response to new places. The atmosphere of Minor County cricket was much less tense than what he had been accustomed to, and he took to his work readily. He quickly became a good umpire, careful, prompt and conscientious, and became aware that he had the reputation of a reliable man.

At the end of each season he applied for promotion, and at the end of the second year he was successful. He knew pretty well what to look forward to—six hours' work, six days a week, for just over four months, work that would keep him on his feet the whole time, and demanding unremitting vigilance and concentration. A superficial respect for his office would be observed, but not for his person, for he would be expected to act as a perambulating cloak-room. His mistakes would be noted, players discontented with his decisions would, behind his back, accuse him of ignorance, prejudice, partisanship, and even corruption. He would be fiercely criticised—expressions like "I never saw such bloody umpiring in my life", expressions which he himself had carelessly uttered in the old days, would be directed against him. On the other hand, here was a decent living, and one that might last him many years, provided that he conserved his health and offended no important interests.

He was, on the first day of his first match, a little nervous. He was surrounded by players he knew, and he felt that their eyes were upon him. But he was quick to realise, and be re-assured by the extraordinary anonymity conferred by the umpire's white coat. He was an official, and for practical purposes impersonal. Players would greet him with "Hello, Ted", or "Glad to see you out again, Ewe-Lamb," and thereafter forget him pretty completely, apart from a few jokes or expostulations between the fall of the wickets and during the intervals. There were a few younger umpires who dramatised their office, and made a spectacular appeal to both crowd and players; but the position of a man with no very definite personality was aloof. So it was with Teddy; the whole current of the game was dependent on him; yet it seemed to flow by him.

This first match was between Gloucester and Middlesex

at Bristol, and it was curious to note the reaction of Jim Revill. Jim was getting as many runs as ever; not quite so daring now, a little less disposed to steal short runs, a shade slower in the field. Gloucester batted first, and Jim had actually been on the field forty minutes before he noticed Teddy at all. It was about three years since they had met. He was as attractive as ever, in a more lean and fine-drawn way, and he looked very little older. But, "You've changed quite a bit, Yule," he said after the first warm greeting. They had a couple of drinks together at the end of the first day, but their talk was all of the past, and thereafter they hardly saw each other off the field. On the final day it fell to Teddy's lot to give Jim out leg-before-wicket, and Jim did not like it. "If that was out, you must have given me a guard outside the off-stump," he said, as he passed Teddy on his way to the pavilion. Teddy apologised, "Sorry, Jim, but I still think you were out." Jim went off early to catch a train; and these were the last words the two old friends ever spoke together.

For that ill-luck, which lies in wait for all who look to popular sports for their living, and which had always singled out Teddy as special victim, was waiting round the corner once again. He got through the first half of the season fairly well, not escaping criticism, but satisfied that no more was falling to his lot than to that of most of his colleagues. Pains in the back troubled him at times, and he often got very tired, for the work was far more severe than with the Minor Counties, with no rests between matches, and long railway journeys sometimes lasting all night. But the harder the work the more money he earned, and he saw his way to saving a good proportion of it. He was leading a very sober life these days, and it was his aim to put by at least forty or fifty pounds every year. By the time he had to retire, in fifteen or twenty years time, he should have nearly a thousand pounds in hand, a sum which would serve to buy him a comfortable annuity so that he could end his days in comfort. The future, it was true, looked grey enough. He was very lonely, for he had made no new friends. Only with Cecil French, and to a lesser degree Jim Revill, had he ever achieved terms of intimate friendship. But he was used to a lonely life, and, as to brighter passages, he found his desires contracting as he grew older. Sometimes he reproached himself with thinking like an old man; but he knew that in spirit he was indeed old. He lived in the present and the past; from the future he asked only security.

As the season progressed his back did not improve, and there were times when he could hardly stand for pain. Sometimes, towards the end of a long day, his vigilance would relax. Twice he made mistakes in calling the over, and once he had to answer an appeal for stumping at a moment when his attention had wandered completely. Obeying the regulations covering such a lapse he gave a verdict of "not out"; but from the grin on the batsman's face and the scowls on those of the fieldsmen he could see clearly that it had not been a case admitting any doubt.

In mid-July he ran into more serious trouble. A midland county with Championship hopes found itself in a tantalising position on the last day of a match. It required less than thirty for victory with all its wickets in hand. But a heavy morning rain only cleared up at about three o'clock, and the wicket was saturated. Before five o'clock, with the water lying on the pitch, there was no question of play, but after that the captains disagreed, each taking the line dictated by his county's interests. The umpires were consulted and agreed that play was not possible, but it was arranged to make another inspection if necessary at a quarter to six. The views of the captains remained irreconcilable, and the inspection was made.

The pitch was a mudheap; one could not lift one's foot without removing cakes of turf. It was clearly impossible for the bowlers to get any foothold at all; nevertheless, the other umpire seemed ready to sanction play. Teddy, however, was quite clear in his mind, and so, as provided by the rules in case of disagreement, the state of things in being continued. This meant that the match was abandoned, and the disappointed captain was furious.

In the pavilion Teddy's colleague observed:

"I think you've made a mistake."

"But it was impossible to stand up, man."

"Maybe. All the same, I think you've made a mistake. That guy's got a hell of a lot of pull."

Teddy's next match was a bad one. In the one after it Somerset were playing the county with which Le Mesurier was now associated. Le Mesurier had at last fallen foul of the Midhampton Committee—ironically enough, the year after Teddy's dismissal. His arrogance and dictatorial methods, on and off the field, had grown with years and finally become insupportable. Much had been endured for the sake of his great prestige and playing ability, but when he insisted that the space in the south stand, immediately behind the wickets, should be roped off and the public excluded, he was attacking the club's revenue, and for the first time met with effective opposition. Having made an issue of it he lacked the finesse to withdraw gracefully, and in consequence was now finishing his cricket career as the captain of the county of his birth.

This implacable man gave no sign of recognising Teddy at all at the outset of the match. Teddy would indeed have been happy to escape his notice throughout. Fortunately he was not called upon to give any decision while his old enemy was at the wicket, and all it seemed had gone well when, at a critical stage on the last day, a Somerset batsman got hold of a half-volley and made a low skimming drive to mid-off—where Le Mesurier, diving at full length, picked up the ball just off the ground. He threw it up in the air; the Somerset batsman stayed in his crease.

Rather belatedly Le Mesurier appealed. Teddy shook his head. He had no doubt that the ball had been scooped off the ground, and his response was instinctive. For the moment he didn't even realise who was concerned in the incident.

Le Mesurier exclaimed angrily: "Are you blind, man? Or just crooked?"

Teddy did not reply. The Somerset batsmen continued his innings. He made 79 not out and just carried his side to victory by two wickets.

Teddy thought that the gratuitous insult would have been sufficient vent for Le Mesurier's feelings. But a few matches later a well-known amateur, with whom he had always had friendly relaxations, came up and spoke to him.

"Feel I ought to tell you, Ewe-Lamb, you've got one or two people up against you. I wouldn't mention it, but if you put in a word in season it might make a difference."

Teddy answered, "I'm very much obliged to you. I suppose you mean Mr. Le Mesurier?"

"Chiefly him. He carries a lot of weight still, you know, and he might get a majority when the appointments come up again. It might be worth your while to approach him tactfully."

Teddy thought a great deal about the matter. He hardly believed that one or two men would have the power to prevent his re-appointment. He was afraid, too, that a direct approach might further antagonise Le Mesurier—the man was touchy as the devil, and previous attempts to placate him had generally made things worse.

However, towards the end of the season he happened to be umpiring in a Festival game in which Le Mesurier was engaged, and on a sudden impulse he took an opportunity to speak to him.

"I was very sorry about that catch at Taunton, sir," he said. "Of course, you were in the best position to know—I should have realised that."

Self-abnegation could go no farther. "That's all right, Lamb," Le Mesurier answered, with a slight relaxation of his usual stiffness. "Glad you realise it now—pity you didn't at the time."

A foolish desire to make sure tempted Teddy to further speech.

"I hope you won't hold it against me, sir."

Le Mesurier's eyes became glassy.

"What exactly do you mean by that?"

"Well—naturally I'm a bit anxious. It's my first year, you see, sir, and perhaps I've made a few mistakes."

"You certainly have."

"I'm hoping you won't count that one against me."

"Lamb, I seem to remember something like this before. If I understand you properly, you're suggesting that because I happen to be the victim of one of these 'mistakes', I'm likely to allow personal feeling to prompt me to get you removed?"

"No, sir, I didn't mean that."

"I don't see what else you could have meant. I'll tell you the truth, since you've asked for it. You haven't struck me as likely to make at all a satisfactory umpire. Practically every one with whom I've discussed the subject is of the same way of thinking. I tell you this so that if the captains are unable to re-appoint you, perhaps you won't put it down to my personal spite. At least, I hope you won't."

"Thank you, sir," said Teddy, looking the man straight in the eyes. "I quite understand."

He turned away feeling a little sick.

Three months passed, and the captains met again. Teddy was not re-appointed, not even in the Minor Counties list.

XLI

SOMEWHERE IN THE northern border of the county of Midhampton lies the town of Warfield, containing some sixteen thousand inhabitants, mostly dependent in some way or another on the two large brickworks situated near the canal. This part of the town is mean and ugly, but the main street, situated on rising ground about half a mile away, is quiet, spacious, and with a decorous simplicity about its prevailing architecture. It had formed part of an important coaching route in other days, and although the main stream of traffic now flows a few miles eastward, it still constitutes a secondary road connecting two great arteries, and retains a lingering shadow of its old character. At the corner near the Market Cross are two inns of some pretension—one, "The Feathers", a Trust House, renovated, smart, and expensive; the other, "The Boot and Saddle", newer and more spacious, but with much more of the public house character, of which it does not seem to be ashamed.

The proprietor at the time of the latter house, a lean elderly man with white hair and a small black moustache, was reading the newspaper in his saloon one morning a few minutes before opening time, when a small man with a greasy felt hat, dusty boots, and an air of defeat, found his way into the room from the hotel entrance. The proprietor looked up from his paper in a suspended way.

"Another five minutes yet," he said.

"That's all right," answered the visitor, "I don't want a drink."

He hesitated, and then, with the other's eyes still on him, stammered on.

"I thought—you might remember me, Mr. Tanner."

The proprietor's hard stare was maintained for a moment, then he put down the paper.

"Well, Ewe-Lamb, I didn't know you. It must be five or six years since you were last up here with the county. You've changed a lot."

Teddy answered, "We don't grow any younger, Joe."

Tanner drew a beer without any comment and pushed it across the bar. "How's the world treating you?" he asked.

"So-so." Teddy fingered the tankard. "Found things a bit tough lately."

"What are you doing now?"

Teddy grinned, showing large gaps between the discoloured teeth that remained. "Resting," he answered. "That's what the actors say."

"Out of a job, eh?" Tanner turned his back for a moment, arranging some bottles on a shelf. "I heard you had dropped out of umpiring."

"Dropped out of pretty nearly everything, the last few years." He drained two thirds of his beer, and began to talk with the rather painful volubility of a man who had grown unused to the sound of his own voice.

"Got a job in a shop for a week or two—Blakers. Couldn't make out the bills quick enough, though—I was never any good at arithmetic. Then there's post office work at Christmas, and sometimes in summer a little Saturday afternoon umpiring—you know, five bob and a cup of tea. Got a day a week coaching too—prep school. But it's been pretty bad lately—the cold's started early this winter. I've spent most of the days in the Public Library—first to come, last to go. They don't let you smoke there—stops you wasting money on cigarettes."

"How did you find your way up here?"

Teddy pulled at the collar of his shirt.

"Been walking round, the last few days. I was at the Union at Cawston last night. Thought I'd give Warfield a look—I got some runs and wickets here in the old days."

Joe Tanner considered. He had been good friends with old Baa Lamb. He ought to try and do something for the chap. He'd been a good cricketer, and as far as he knew always steady. Yet there was a look about him now that was not promising—it might be better if he sent him on his way with a ten bob note.

"It isn't that I'm afraid of work," added Teddy.

"Well, Ewe-Lamb, I know you've had bad luck. I'd like to give you a leg-up."

He hesitated, but presently went one. "I could give you a sort of a job. There's no one looking after the billiard-room. Two good tables and sometimes the gentlemen are a bit careless. There'd be nothing much in it—I'd find you a bed and food, but I couldn't do better than five bob a week. Of course, there'd be tips now and then."

Teddy answered eagerly. "That would suit me, Joe. When could I start?"

"Right away." Tanner pulled up the flap and emerged from behind the bar. "Come along round, I'll show you the place."

XLII

IT WAS, at least, security of a fashion. The work was not arduous. It consisted partly of looking after the tables, brushing them, ironing them occasionally, and putting on the covers after play, discreetly removing glasses placed on the polished mahogany tops, dissuading pot-valiant gentlemen from too enterprising shots imperilling the cloth. He did the marking when he was allowed to, saw that the cues were provided with tips, and generally kept the room clean. It was his business to encourage the players to order drinks—this with a few exceptions did not prove difficult—and to fetch them. Sometimes, when there was a rush, he was called on to help in the saloon bar. Generally he made ten or twelve shillings a week in tips.

His clients consisted mainly of people of the commercial class, of all ages. They soon found out who he was, and were, on the whole, very willing to show a patronising kindness to one who had once been a person of consequence. But their patronage generally took the form of standing him drinks, and Teddy could never bring himself to explain how greatly he would have preferred the fourpences or eightpences, to the bitters or whiskies that were offered him so liberally. Finally he ceased to have the preference. He had hardly any life outside "The Boot and Saddle", no friends apart from billiard-room acquaintances, and few outside temptations to spend money. On the whole, however, he was not unhappy. By degrees he almost forgot about cricket, as anything more than the page he first turned to in the season when he managed to get hold of a newspaper.

His health was not always very good. His lumbago now was chronic—a permanent disability that was seldom acutely painful. He had been at "The Boot and Saddle" a little over a year when he began to get his headaches. They seemed to centre round the old injury he had got in Barbados, and they were very bad at first, so much so that he went to a doctor, who gave him prescriptions which brought temporary relief. But this did not last long, and the trouble with his head settled down into a chronic affliction, like his lumbago. He found, however, that alcohol gave him a real alleviation. He began to buy drinks with his own money, when he was not being treated, but they brought no real elevation to his spirits—only a remission of pain.

Early in the second spring Joe Tanner retired from the business to devote himself to golf and gardening, and a comfortable little home he had bought a mile out of town. The new proprietor, Mr. Hussey, was a hearty, broad-faced, youngish man, who had promised before taking over that he intended to make no changes in the staff. But he had the knack of getting something extra out of his employees, and Teddy found himself called upon for more and more work in the bar. By degrees he was practically transformed into a saloon waiter; the billiard room was kept locked, and gentlemen wishing to use it had to ask to have it opened. Teddy gave less attention to the tables, and that class of custom fell away.

The change was a bad one for him. The work was now much harder, and he did not find it easy to get about briskly. He took to drinking more and more in the middle of the day as well as in the evening. He was conscious of the intensely practical eye of his new employer on him, and had to simulate some sort of energy.

He began to have little accidents. One evening he stumbled over the outstretched foot of a seated customer and spilt a tray containing three beers, two whiskies and a port—luckily on to the floor. When the house closed that night Mr. Hussey spoke to him. "There was four and eightpence'orth of liquor on that tray. To say nothing of two glasses smashed. 'Fraid you'll have to pay that back, my lad."

The increased work told on his nerves, and his headaches became worse. There came a time when he found that beer was no longer doing its work. He stood it for a little while, and then one night, in acute agony, he began drinking whisky. He had already had three or four beers, and had not reckoned with his own nervous exhaustion. He suddenly found himself quite drunk. Coming up to the bar he was unable to remember a simple order.

"I'm not well, Mr. Hussey," he managed to say. "Have to knock off for tonight."

Mr. Hussey's glance was of the sort that nothing escapes. "All right, Lamb," he said. "You go to bed."

He was dismissed the next morning. "No hard feelings, I hope," said Mr. Hussey. "But you're not really fit for this work. Take my advice and rest off before you go for another job—get your health better. And, if you don't mind a word in season, you'll hop on that wagon for a bit."

XLIII

IT WAS NOW NOVEMBER—a bad time for finding employment. He did, however, manage to get a job at a public house in a poor quarter of the town—what in an earlier age would have been called a potman's job. The place was sordid, the wage was poor, and he had to sleep out. Also there were no tips, but the landlord took a generous view of his assistant's requirements in the matter of beer. In this environment Teddy, who had maintained a degree of self respect at "The Boot and Saddle", coarsened rapidly. He felt the need of compensation, and his normal taciturnity became varied by bursts of boastful loquacity, and sometimes of quarrelsomeness. He became involved in one or two silly, rather unreal fights, and then one which, while perhaps silly, was by no means unreal. Through this, in which he lost a tooth and got a badly split lip, he became enmeshed in an affair with the barmaid. This was a maid hardly younger than himself, unclean and unattractive, but shrewish and fiercely possessive. The wear and tear wrought on his system by his passages with this harridan was the chief cause of his decision to leave Warfield in the spring.

His idea was to go on the tramp for a few weeks. His lumbago had been very bad during the winter, and he believed that plenty of exercise now the weather was warmer would put him on his feet again. He would sleep at the Unions, doing what work was required of him, and get what other work he could, or take what food might be offered him, from the people from whom he solicited work; then return to Midhampton and look for a regular job when he felt better.

It seemed a sensible plan. But he had, perhaps, overestimated his stamina, and his luck was poor. On the second stage of his journey, walking from Cawston to Midhampton, where he intended spending no more time than was required for admission to the Union, he was overtaken by a heavy rain on top of the Common. There was no shelter among the gorse, and by the time he got into the town and reached the workhouse he was badly chilled. The next day he could not get up, and was transferred to the Infirmary. It was pneumonia, and he lay in bed for a month. When, at the end of six weeks, he was discharged he had not got much strength back.

He took a room in the street in which he had lived the winter after his retirement. It was a cheaper one than at that time though—a small top room with no furniture but a verminous bed and two chairs. On the landing outside was a gas ring and oven, uncertainly responsive to pennies. At this he was permitted to do his own cooking, when he could afford to buy anything to cook.

He had—and it was a small satisfaction—succeeded in achieving anonymity. Nobody at all at the workhouse had recognised him, and in his slum he was just "Mr. Lamb" —"old Mr. Lamb" he was often called, when spoken of in the third person. This loss of identity he had, however, to abandon when after a week of unsuccessful attempts to find work, he went before the Public Assistance Committee.

His application for relief was turned down. He was unqualified for unemployment benefit, and he was not aged or disabled. The workhouse was indicated as a possible resource for him. But one of the members of the Committee remembered him, and a day or two later Teddy was given a job—the delivery of newspapers, morning and evening, in one of the better sections of the town. The wage was a boy's wage—just sufficient to find him something to eat when his very small room rent had been paid. But it only took up about three hours of the day, as much as he felt fit for at the time. And his extreme poverty did have the beneficial effect of keeping him off drink.

The greater part of each day he spent in the newspaper and reference room of the Public Library. But one warm day late in June he found himself feeling better than he had for a long time. There was a home match at the County Ground, and he experienced a sudden nostalgia for the old place. More from a sense of shame than any other cause, he had deliberately cut himself off from everyone and everything to do with the ground. He had had his life there, with all of its setbacks a very successful one, and there above all he felt unwilling to exhibit his distress. But this morning it struck him forcibly that his attitude had been surly and over-sensitive. The county owed him a debt, when all was said; it could hardly let him sink to the extreme of poverty, and he had no reason to feel shame in accepting whatever might be offered him from that source.

It was, however, almost as much a sudden desire to see some cricket that sent him, after a brief internal debate, to the ground. He could not, of course, afford a shilling. The gate-keeper at the turnstile at the North entrance was unfamiliar to him. He nodded uncertainly and made to push his way in.

"Morning," he said, "You know me, I suppose."

The gate-man looked at him and replied, with more candour than courtesy, "No, my lad. I don't."

"I'm Ted Lamb—Ewe-Lamb they used to call me here."

"Is that so?" retorted the man. "Pleased to meet you."

It was not clear to Teddy whether the gate-keeper did not believe him, or simply had never heard of him.

"Aren't you going to let me in?" he asked.

"I'll let you in," he answered. "It's a bob, you know."

"But, good lord!" Teddy expostulated. "I tell you I'm Ted Lamb. Do you mean to say that after serving the county for twenty odd years I've got to pay to see a day's cricket?"

"Sorry, I've no instructions. You'd better get a note from the secretary."

"Well, let me go and see the Secretary."

"I can't let you in without paying. You write a letter to the Secretary. If you get a note from him it will be all right."

"Listen," said Teddy. "Have you ever heard of me?"

"I ain't been here long. I kind of remember the name, though. But how do I know you're who you say you are?"

Teddy lost his temper.

"You silly sod. How the bloody hell did you ever get the job?"

"None of that language—or I'll get a policeman to talk to you. You run along home."

"Let me in!" shouted Teddy. "You let me get the other side, or I'll show you some language."

Very few people were coming in at this entrance, and the scene so far had not been a public one. But at this moment an elderly gentleman approached the gate.

"Come, Fraser, what's all this trouble about?" he demanded, not without self-importance.

Teddy turned and recognised him at once. "Mr. Gladman, you know me, don't you? Seems to me people in Midhampton have short memories. This man won't let me in, and as good as called me a liar when I told him who I was."

The old gentleman scrutinised Teddy.

"Your face *is* familiar," he said. "But I can't quite place it—why, hang it, you're Ewe-Lamb!"

Teddy answered humbly. "Yes, sir. I know I've altered quite a bit."

"My dear fellow," Mr. Gladman exclaimed, warmly apologetic, and he took his arm. "I'm shocked that this should have happened. Come along in."

He turned to the gate-keeper. "Lamb was one of our stalwarts for more years than I like to remember. You take a good look at him and let him in whenever he wants to come. Mr. Gaul would not be very pleased to hear about this."

Teddy followed the buffer into the ground, and accompanied him at a slow pace towards the pavilion. Mr. Gladman's affable but by no means stupid glance rested on him more than once. Eventually he took him into the pavilion, and deposited him in the professionals' enclosure. "You'll find some old friends here," he announced at large. "Boys, I expect most of you remember Ewe-Lamb."

Teddy passed an uncomfortable hour. There were several new faces—had he ever been so beefy as these young men, he wondered—and of those remaining from his later days none had been particular cronies of his. Men like Heath, and Beal, and Farrar said a few words to him, but it was clear that his shabbiness and seediness was an affront to them. Lumley had retired—the last link with his early days. It was a relief when Levison, who had been playing a good innings, got out at last. He recognised Teddy with unaffected pleasure, and sat talking to him till lunch time, finally carrying him off to eat with the rest of the players.

In the late afternoon, when the Midhampton side was in the field, Mr. Gaul came up to him.

"You're not looking too well, Lamb," he said, after a few minutes small talk. "I hope you're doing all right."

"Not too well, sir," Teddy replied. "I'm finding it hard to make do. You see, I never had any other trade."

Mr. Gaul nodded. "I know. You had a lot of bad luck when you were playing, too. Are you looking for a job?"

"I'd take anything I could get."

"I was talking about you to Mr. Gladman this morning. You see, Lamb, we recognise we owe you something. But the county simply can't *make* jobs. Everyone knows what our finances are like. It's only the generosity of a few people that enables us to carry on at all. And we can't bank on that for ever."

"It'd be a bad day for Midhampton if the county had to close down, sir."

"We're all hoping it won't come to that. But you see the difficulty—if we were flourishing we could offer you something decent. As it is, the only possible opening—I don't suppose you'd care about it."

"What is it, sir?"

"Well; selling score cards. The usual thing, what you get depending on sales. It's a pretty wretched living but it is a living as long as the season lasts. And perhaps later, if we strike better times, or when anyone leaves, we could find you something better."

Teddy swallowed his pride.

"I'd be very glad of it, sir. I do need the money."

XLIV

INTO THE SUNSHINE, round the arena, the melting asphalt verge burning his feet—"Card! Last wicket down—Card! Last wicket down—Card!" Back to the dark little printing office and the clatter of the ancient machine, belching out more pasteboard slips or adding an afterthought, at the fall of each wicket, to the unsold cards returned. Sometimes the bookstall would give him some "Cricketers" to take round, or a souvenir of the All India tour, or postcards—"Portrait of the Midhampton and All-Indian teams, twopence." He was diffident at first, but quickly became inured, and raucous. A small hunched figure, without dignity. Very rarely he was recognised, and sometimes a kindly person told him not to worry about the change. Once he got half a crown that way. It was easy come, easy go, what there was of it. He still worked on his newspaper job, and, on match days, when he had earned enough to buy himself a decent supper, he spent the rest at one of the bars on the ground. He did not get paid till the end of the day, but he always knew how he stood, and the people at the bars found they could trust him. A good day was a day when he got tight. On August Bank Holiday he could hardly sell his cards quickly enough, but he managed to find time to slip in a drink every half hour or so. At five o'clock he was almost incapable, and the crowd laughed at him as he lurched around. "Good old Ted," someone said. "Another little one won't do you any harm."

The matter came to the attention of the Committee,

and Teddy was warned. He went more carefully for the rest of the season, with the result that he had a pound or two in hand to help him through the winter.

It did not last long. He found no occupation with which to supplement his newspaper delivery, and he now found himself quite unable to do without drink. Often he would go without food so as to have a few pence to put down to pay for his standing in a public house of an evening. He would buy his half-pint, take a few sips, sparingly, and manœuvre for contacts which might lead to his being treated. His voice took on a wheedling tone. Frequenters of certain houses got accustomed to his slight, bowed, listless figure, down at heel and not over-clean, sidling up to them and opening a conversation. He did not actually beg, but he had a trick of draining his glass at what seemed the best moment, and exclaiming, "Wish I could afford more of this—warms you up." He often did well enough, especially when after a few beers he felt released beyond the point of feeling shame at revealing his identity. But here and there he was found a nuisance, and met with rebuffs. The assistants at one house were instructed not to serve him, and when one day, unaware of this, he appeared in it, he was put out, not too gently.

As the winter drew on, his life became harder. He had no longer an overcoat, and his first delivery, often made before it was light in the season when the days are shortest, became a frozen and fumbling agony. He caught an obstinate cold early in December, turning to a cough he could not shake off. Somehow he got through the Christmas season, and collected his tips, but the last morning of the old year, after a terrible cough-shaken night, found him feverish and unable to get up.

He lay in bed for three weeks, depending for food, when he was able to eat any, almost entirely on the charity of the working-class family who occupied the ground floor. He had just enough money intact for his rent during this period. His job was being held for him, and somehow he struggled through to the spring. When he reported to the county ground he was a wreck of what he had been—hollow-chested, round-shouldered, shuffling, painfully thin. He had given up shaving (except on Sundays) and to a large extent, the use of soap and water. What was the use? It was over two years since he had been able to buy any clothes. He had been accustomed to patch up those he had with some care up to the time of his illness. But after that nothing had seemed to matter, and his appearance was now unequivocally disreputable. "You ought to be in hospital, Ewe-Lamb," said the man in charge of the printing office on his reappearance. "You don't look strong enough for work."

Nor, in truth, was he strong enough. He had too much walking to do on match days—three miles, morning and evening, delivering papers, and possibly twice that amount round the ground. Still, he was getting better money again, and he kept up his strength in the familiar way.

One day, during a lunch interval, he fell in with two men he had no recollection of ever having seen before, but who seemed to know all about his career, and became warmingly garrulous about it. They had clearly been drinking a good deal already, and they carried him off to the bar, cards and all, and treated him largely. Play recommenced, an hour passed, and Teddy eventually returned to the printing office late, reeking of beer, and without the cards, which he had forgotten in the bar, or their money equivalent. That was the end of the job.

Most of his days, thereafter, he passed stretched out on his bed, not so much thinking as allowing memories to pass unchecked through his brain. He hardly ever read now; he did not seem able to concentrate on more than a few pages at a time. In fine weather, when a home match was on, he would struggle round to the ground, where he had still free admission. He would take a seat near some unsuspecting person, get into talk, and make himself as interesting as he could, with his expert comments on the game. Perhaps the stranger would make some inquiry, perhaps Teddy would start it himself; but whichever way it was, the tale would always come out—his own tale. It became stereotyped, almost to a word. He grew to like telling it, for its own sake—he had acquired, prematurely, the reminiscent garrulity of old age. But the purpose always lay behind and he was successful almost as often as not. The stranger might experience genuine pity or a desire to shake off this distressful person who had begun as if he were a "character", but was ending as a cadging bore.

There was another fine August Bank Holiday, and he had a good morning. Warmed by four or five beers, and heartened by two or three shillings he had picked up, he took up a standing position near the sight screen, and began giving a kind of running commentary on the game. Someone called out, "Sit down, you old fool"; but the crowd was in a holiday humour and willing to listen to him—"Let him alone; it's only old Ted." When he showed signs of flagging, some fool fetched him a pint of beer from the bar, and he drank it, yards out on the playing pitch, with his head tossed back, so that he spilt a lot on his face and shoulders. A policeman came up.

"Come on, get out of here."

Teddy looked at him drunkenly.

"You can't order me out. I'm one of the players."

A few people in the crowd guffawed. The policeman took Teddy by the arm.

"Come along," he said peremptorily. "No more nonsense."

In the pavilion Mr. Gaul, talking to a member, had noticed the later stages of the incident. So had the member, who said:

"That's old Ted making a nuisance of himself again."

Mr. Gaul nodded.

"Yes. We'll have to bar him from the ground, I'm afraid."

"It seems rather a tragedy, after his splendid career—to be pushed out of the ground by a policeman."

"It is a tragedy. And do you know, I'm not at all sure it's entirely his own fault."

XLV

TEDDY walked home very slowly the next morning. He had tried both gates, and had been refused admission at both. Last night he had drunk away all the money he had left, had gone to bed drunk, awakened from a heavy sleep about one, tossed in agony of body and mind for three or four hours, and finally fallen into a second sleep from which he had not awakened till after nine. Long after the hour for his morning delivery, but he had done nothing about it. Probably he could fix things up.

He reached his top room, and flung himself on the bed. This last disgrace, in the chilly pitiless sobriety that was his this morning, had reawakened a shame which he had thought was dead. He knew too, with a lucid certainty, that there was nothing he could do about it, no way of re-establishing his dignity. As recently as a year ago, he could have pulled up. But now he was hopelessly dependent on drink, he could not get through the day without it.

He could feel the need tugging at him at the moment. And he had no money with which to satisfy it.

Was it his fault? He wondered, unconsciously echoing Mr. Gaul's doubts. Had there always been some fundamental weakness about his character? Even in his mood of self-chastisement, he was doubtful. Surely he had shown, more than once, determination in conquering obstacle after obstacle, in becoming a professional cricketer at all, in making himself a good bowler by dint of unremitting practice, in contriving his "Q-bowling", in turning himself into a spin bowler when his "Q-bowling" was stopped, in successfully working up his batting when his bowling arm let him down. Was that the record of a weakling? At what point in time had the change come, his defences broken down, his will and character been undermined, so that he was left alone and exposed to a wretched old age? Was it perhaps that all men had only a certain reserve of energy and resistance to draw on, and that he had by ill chance and evil circumstances, been compelled to expend his too prodigally? Or had the War, those shiftless dangerous years, unprofitably squandered in the critical prime of his youth, taken its belated toll? Certainly it was then that he had learned to drink, and his generally successful contest against a besetting temptation had only ended in capitulation almost the other day.

"I should never have worked at a pub," he muttered.

He got up, and pulled out the square canvas box containing all his remaining possessions, from under the bed. Not much left—winter pants and vests, his extra shirt, two pairs of socks. The rest was mostly his scrap-books, full of press cuttings, the record of the dash he had cut in the world. His *Wisdens* had all gone now—the one in which he had figured as one of the Cricketers of the Year only last winter. They had commanded good prices, the equivalent of gallons of beer, barrels almost in the case of some of the earlier editions. But the scrap-books had no market value.

He turned over the pages lovingly; smoothing down the faded and discoloured strips. There was his picture at twenty-one—he remembered the Brighton photographer for whom he had posed. Had he ever looked so fresh and vital as that? Here were the records of his great year—the "Q-bowling" year—overflowing into a second volume; reports, articles by him and about him, action pictures, cartoons, that front page in the *Daily Mirror*. Here was a group taken in Barbados, everybody hot but cheerful looking—perhaps the beginning of his losing struggle dated from that tour. Here was an enthusiastic report from the *Telegraph* of his best feat as a slow bowler; here was the record of his first century, made the day after he parted with Desirée. If Desirée could see him now! He had still been young, and felt young then. Yet it was not so many years ago.

He shut the last of the books, leaving them on the bed where he had been sitting. It would have been better not to have touched them—was there any one in the world to whom they would be even of the slightest interest?

It was growing dark. He could do with a cup of tea. He went out on to the landing and lit the gas-ring. The light just purred in a circular blue flame—it needed a penny. He went downstairs in the hope of borrowing one. But the house was empty.

Then he remembered that he had slipped a few coppers into his waistcoat yesterday, against this emergency. He found them—there were three—and trudged up the darkening stairs.

An impulse which he had felt many times during the last year suddenly came back to him with irresistible force. Why not? He had never lacked courage. Here was an opportunity—an empty house, to which no one was likely to return for half an hour at least. He knew everyone's routine. There was time enough and to spare.

He hesitated for a moment on the landing. Then he put a penny in the meter slot, turned the knob and heard the coin clatter down. The blue ring leaped into a pale yellow vitality. But it wasn't enough—not enough to be sure. He put in the second coin and the third.

It was almost completely dark now. Quietly, meditatively almost, he opened the oven door.

EPITAPH

(As from Wisden's Cricketer's Almanack)

LAMB, EDWIN WILSON, for many years Midhampton's best professional bowler and in later years a sound and reliable batsman, died at Midhampton under tragic circumstances on August 8th.

The son of A. E. Lamb, the great Midhampton all-rounder of the early nineties and the early years of the present century, E. W., in spite of his lack of robust physique, had enjoyed considerable success as a right-hand medium-paced bowler when he startled the cricket world with his "Q-bowling" in 1923. Lamb's name has been eclipsed by more famous exponents of this type of leg-theory, and many have forgotten that he was the originator of it. In that year he achieved remarkable results, taking 187 wickets, at 15.98 apiece, but afterwards he was less successful, and after a few years lost his bowling altogether. No doubt the strain of playing for a weak bowling county proved in the end too great for him.

Altogether, in first class matches for Midhampton, Lamb took 1,109 wickets at the cost of 22.33 runs apiece, and scored 9,216 runs for an average of 18.43.

Lamb never played against Australia, but he went to the West Indies with the M.C.C. team in the winter of 1923–24. He played only a small part in the tour, however, receiving an early injury which kept him out of the remaining games. He made two appearances for the Players at Lords and Newborough, both in 1923.

With an easy action and thorough command of length, **Lamb** possessed all the assets of a fine bowler, being able to spin the ball, swing it both ways, and to change his pace and flight in a most deceptive manner. It was perhaps his weakness that he was too prone to experiment. Good judges of the game have suggested that if he had settled down and perfected himself in one particular type of bowling he would have made an even bigger name for himself.

A man whose batting potentialities were only realised comparatively late in his career—he had been playing for Midhampton fourteen years before he made the first of his eleven hundreds—Lamb was in addition a very capable slip-fielder. Born at Midhampton on January 6th, 1890.

OTHER OUTSTANDING BOOKS
IN THIS NEW SERIES

Published by
Howard Baker Publishers Limited
in association with
REMPLOY LIMITED
NEWCASTLE-UNDER-LYME, STAFFORDSHIRE

THE WAY OF A TRANSGRESSOR

Negley Farson

THE WAY OF A TRANSGRESSOR, the first volume of Negley Farson's autobiography provides a fascinating personal view of Europe and America between the wars. When first published in 1935, it enjoyed a huge popular success, running into nine impressions in twenty-one months.

Few indeed are the books which deserve immortality, but this is certainly one of them. It is the enthralling, thrilling—often moving—record of an adventurous life that should find a place on every bookshelf. It is without doubt a book to read again, again—and again.

---

09 308350 5

35/- £1.75

MORNING FOR MR. PROTHERO

Jane Oliver

Thomas Prothero, the eminent surgeon, is ill, close to death. As he lies inert, his mind wanders over past events and associations: Nanny's cottage at Glaury Syke, dearest of all his childhood memories; his son, Andrew, driven out of his mind by shell-shock during the Great War; his daughter, Mary. . . or do these memories constitute reality? What does Nanny mean when she tells him meaningfully that he has 'crossed the border'? And what of the mysterious Dr. Grant and his hospital full of people from Mr. Prothero's past?

'There are more things in heaven and earth, Horatio, than are dreamt of in your philosophy,' says Hamlet to his sceptical friend. Mr. Prothero's scepticism, the product of a lifetime's professional knowledge of pain and grief, proves, like Horatio's, to be inadequate to deal with the events that follow.

---

09 304490 9

26/- £1.30